Enid Blyton

WINTER STORIES

Look out for all of these enchanting story collections

by *Enid Blyton*

Enid Blyton
WINTER STORIES

Hodder
Children's
Books

HODDER CHILDREN'S BOOKS

This collection first published in Great Britain in 2018
by Hodder & Stoughton

7 9 10 8 6

A CIP catalogue record for this book is available from the British Library.

ISBN 978 1 444 94255 2

Printed and bound in Great Britain by Clays Ltd, Elcograf S.p.A.

The paper and board used in this book are made from wood from
responsible forests.

MIX
Paper from
responsible sources
FSC® C104740

Hodder Children's Books
An imprint of Hachette Children's Group
Part of Hodder and Stoughton
Carmelite House
50 Victoria Embankment
London EC4Y 0DZ

An Hachette UK Company
www.hachette.co.uk
www.hachettechildrens.co.uk

Contents

A Little Snow House

A Little Snow House

THE SNOW was deep on the ground. Pip and Jinky had built two snowmen, and thrown snowballs at one another till they were tired.

They thought they would build a snow house for themselves. 'You know, it's warmer under the snow than on top,' Pip told Jinky. 'So if we build a house under the snow, we shall be as warm as if we have blankets on. Aunt Twinkle told me that last week.'

'Ooooh yes, let's build a snow house then,' said Jinky. 'I'd love that.'

So they began to build a snow house. They burrowed deep in a snowdrift, and made a big hole there. Then they began to build a nice house of snow. They made the walls, and patted the snow down as they built them.

'Now we'll put on the roof,' said Jinky. 'We'll make it nice and round. It will be easier to build that way.'

'We'll make holes in the walls for windows,' said Pip. 'But not very big ones, because we don't want the cold air to come in. And we'll make a little door too. Isn't this fun, Jinky?' They worked very hard, and when teatime came the house was quite finished. The two pixies looked at it proudly. They were hot with their work, and the little snow house seemed cosy and snug.

'Let's live here!' said Pip. 'Let's fetch our beds in and sleep here. We shall be as warm as toast.'

'Well, the house will only take one bed,' said Jinky. 'I'll get mine. We can cuddle up together.'

They put the bed in the snow house. Then they sat on it, eating the jam sandwiches that Aunt Twinkle had given them. 'It's a bit cold after all,' said Pip with a sudden shiver. 'Let's make a little fireplace, and put some twigs there for a fire. That will be very snug. Then we'll curl up in bed and go to sleep.'

So they made a cheerful fire, curled up in bed and fell asleep. But alas, they soon woke up, and felt a cold drip-drip falling down on them. The house was vanishing fast! They were wet through.

'Oh, what's happened?' cried Pip. 'Jinky, quick, what has happened to our little house?'

Well – you know what had happened, don't you? Funny old Pip and Jinky! It wasn't very clever to build a fire in a snow house, was it?

It's Really True!

It's Really True!

ONCE UPON a time the chestnut tree complained loudly because its buds didn't like the cold.

'The frost comes at night and nips my big buds with icy fingers!' said the chestnut tree, creaking loudly in the winter wind. 'What's the use of growing new leafbuds if the frost kills them one by one? I shall have no leaves left at all next spring. Little folk, come and do something about it!'

So the elves came, tiny creatures who looked after flowers and leaves, who polished the shining petals of the celandines when they blossomed, and rubbed up the little coppery beetles that ran among the grasses in the summer.

'We can wrap your baby leaves in cotton wool,' said the elves. 'We'll get some for you.'

So they did, and soon every tiny chestnut leaf was wrapped warmly in soft cotton wool; but still the chestnut tree complained loudly.

'The frost still nips my leafbuds, right through the cotton wool,' said the big tree. 'I tell you, I shall have no leaves at all. Do something, little folk, or we chestnuts will be bare all summertime!'

So the elves held a meeting, and they made up their minds to paint the big fat buds with sticky glue.

'Nothing like a good coat of glue to keep away the fingers of Jack Frost!' said the elves, and they sat up all night and painted glue over each fat bud.

When Jack Frost came along to pinch the buds with his cold fingers, he didn't like the glue, and he left them alone. So they grew bigger and fatter, and when the right time came they burst out of their glue-coats, grew out of the brown scales that held them, and put out little green fingers which were still wrapped in cotton wool.

Well, any boy and girl knows all this: I should think there is hardly anyone who hasn't picked the fat chestnut buds, felt their stickiness, and put the twigs into water to watch the green fingers unfurl.

Now the plane tree thought all this was a very good idea. It grew next to the chestnut tree, and Jack Frost used to come and pinch the plane tree's buds as well. How they trembled when they felt his cold fingers turning them black and shrivelling them up.

'What am I to do?' said the plane tree. 'I have my leafbuds wrapped up so well. The tiny leaves are wrapped in a quilt of soft silky down to keep them warm. They are covered up well in tiny scales that are protected with soft fur. And the outer case of the bud is lined with sticky gum, as strong as any mackintosh.'

'You grow your buds too small,' said the chestnut tree. 'Grow them fat and big like mine – and when the bitter days of the New Year come, they will be strong.'

'It's on the cold days of autumn that my buds feel the cold so much,' said the plane tree. 'What else can I do for them? They cannot be more warmly wrapped up than they already are.'

'Ask the little folk,' said the chestnut tree. 'What are they for if not to help us?' So the plane tree called the elves and told them its troubles.

'You must think of some plan to protect my baby leaves in the autumn,' said the plane tree. 'It is then they feel the cold, and they become so weak that they do not grow well in the New Year. What can I do?'

This was a puzzle. After all, the plane tree already wrapped its leaves in down, and covered them with furry scales. The sticky gum inside their outer case was very strong too. Really there seemed nothing else to do to help the weak baby leaves.

And then an elf had a bright idea. She whispered it to the others. 'Can it be done? It's never been done before! It will take us a long, long time – but we'll try it!' they said.

The elves flew that night to the plane tree, which was still covered with its summer leaves. The elves worked very hard indeed, all night long – and what do you think they did?

They took every leaf from its twig. They hollowed out the leafstalk at the bottom, making it round and large and empty. And then, instead of fitting back each leaf in the place it grew, they carefully fitted the end of the hollowed out stalk over the little new leafbuds that were already showing on the twigs!

'The leafstalks fit over next year's buds like little caps!' said an elf, pleased. 'I say, isn't this a good idea! The little buds will be well protected now. Jack Frost can hunt all he likes for the buds on the plane tree, but he won't find them! They're all hidden at the bottom of the stalks of the autumn leaves!'

The elves flew away, tired out with their night's work. Jack Frost came along at night, hunting for tender leafbuds to nip. He came to the plane tree – and how he stared!

'I can't see a single bud on the tree!' he said. 'Not one! Where are the next year's buds? I can see the autumn leaves – but not a bud is to be seen, though there are plenty on the other trees!'

He hunted up and down the plane tree, but he couldn't find the buds. They were too well hidden under the leafstalks, which fitted over them most perfectly.

After that Jack Frost didn't bother to hunt for plane buds any more. They nestled under the bottom of the old leafstalks, safe and sound, warm and cosy. And when the leaves fell off there were tiny buds underneath, well-grown and strong, ready to burst into new leaves in next year's spring.

This sounds like a fairy story, doesn't it? That's what everybody says. And yet – it's a very funny thing, but it's really true that the leafstalks are hollowed out to fit over the new-growing little buds on every plane tree! Will you look and see, when the plane tree has grown its big leaves, and is changing colour in the autumn?

Don't forget. You won't see a single bud on the tree – but pull away a leaf and you'll find a new bud nestling underneath. Isn't it a clever idea?

The Sparrow
Children

The Sparrow Children

ONCE IN the very cold weather, the young sparrows could not get enough to eat. They were not yet a year old, and they were not as clever as the older sparrows at finding seeds and bits and scraps.

'We will go to our fathers and mothers, who fed us in the nest last year, and see if they will help us,' said Beaky, the biggest young sparrow.

So they flew off to where the older sparrows sat on the barn roof, waiting for the farm hens to be fed. Then there was a chance of flying down and stealing a few grains of corn.

'There are our fathers and mothers,' said Tailer, a

tiny sparrow. 'Mother! Don't you remember me?'

The big brown sparrow he spoke to looked at him in surprise. 'Oh, you are the naughty little sparrow that would keep trying to fly from the nest before you were allowed to!' she said. 'Yes – I do believe you are! What do you want?'

'Please, Mother, we young sparrows are getting more and more hungry in this frosty weather,' said Tailer. 'We want you to give us food as you used to do when we were first out of the nest.'

'Good gracious! We can't do that now that you are nearly a year old!' said the older sparrow. 'You must look after yourselves!'.

The young sparrows were sad and disappointed. Now what were they to do?

A small brownie, who was running by, stopped when he saw the unhappy sparrows.

'What's the matter?' he said. They told him, and he nodded his head.

'Many people are hungry now,' he said, 'as well as

birds. But I am very lucky. I have plenty of food stored away – enough to share with you if you like.'

'Oh, you *are* kind!' cried the sparrows. 'May we come now?'

'Yes,' said the brownie. 'You may come once a day, at dinnertime. I will cook enough potatoes in their skins for all of us, and I will bake enough bread for us all too. Come along!'

They flew on to his small shoulders, and on to his red-capped head, chirruping gaily. He took them to a small house set right underneath a bramble bush, so well hidden that nobody could see it if they passed by.

'Now,' said the brownie, getting some hot potatoes out of the oven, 'here we are! Potatoes for everyone!'

He looked around his room. There was only one chair. He pointed to his bookcase and the sofa. 'The boy sparrows can sit on the bookcase and the girls on the sofa-back,' he said. 'But, dear me – you all look exactly alike to me! However am I going to tell one from another?'

'I'm a boy sparrow,' said Tailer, sitting on the bookcase. 'And Beaky's a boy sparrow too. But Toppy, Flick, Feathers and Fluff are girl sparrows. All the rest are boys.'

The brownie stared at them. 'I shall never know which is which,' he said, 'and I do want to know you all properly. *I* know! I will give the boy sparrows little black bibs to wear! That will always show me which are the boys.'

He took eight little black bibs from a drawer, and put them on the boy sparrows. They were delighted. They really did feel grand. The girls wanted them too, but the brownie shook his head. 'No,' he said, 'if you *all* wear black bibs I'll be just as much muddled as before.'

He gave each sparrow some potato and a handful of crumbs. They were so hungry that they gobbled them up at once.

'Can we keep our black bibs on?' begged the boy sparrows, when they had finished. 'We do feel so grand in them.'

'If you like,' said the brownie, smiling. They did look so funny with the bibs on. So they all few off, and the boy sparrows showed their new bibs very proudly to everyone.

Each day they flew to the brownie's, and each day he fed them until the warm weather came.

'Now you can feed yourselves,' he said. 'But come again next year, as many of you as you like, and I'll help you; but in return, please bring me as much thistledown as you can in the autumn, because I need plenty for my eiderdowns and cushions!'

So in the autumn the sparrows hunted for thistledown for the brownie, and in the cold New Year weather he fed them with all kinds of food.

And they wore their bibs – and still do! You don't believe it? Well, please look carefully at all the sparrows you see. Those that have black bibs under their chins are the boy, or cock, sparrows – and those that have no bibs are the girls, known as hen sparrows.

The boy sparrows always begin to wear them in the New Year, so you will see plenty of them. And now you will always know cock and hen sparrows when you see them!

A Peep Into the
Magic Mirror

A Peep Into the
Magic Mirror

JENNIFER WOKE up with a jump. She sat up in bed. Goodness gracious! What was all that noise?

She reached over to her brother's bed and woke him too. 'Benjy! Wake up! There's such a noise!'

Benjy sat up in alarm. Bells were ringing, someone was blowing a trumpet and there was the noise of gongs being banged loudly.

'Oh, Jennifer – how silly of us! It's the people welcoming in the New Year,' said Benjy at last. 'You know Mummy told us – everyone was going to ring bells and bang gongs at midnight.'

'So she did – and I'd quite forgotten,' said Jennifer.

'Goodness, I was awfully frightened.'

She got out of bed and leant out of the window with her eiderdown round her. 'There are lights everywhere – people with lamps and lanterns. And there's Mr Brown banging his gong – and I do believe that's Mr Trent blowing a trumpet. How funny in the middle of the night!'

Then she jumped in fright because a low voice spoke in her ear. 'Excuse me – may I come in for a minute? They think they're welcoming me in, but really I feel rather scared!'

Jennifer drew back, wondering and a little alarmed. Who was sitting in the tree outside her window? She soon knew.

In came someone who looked like a small child, with fair curly hair and a white robe to his knees with a girdle round his waist. Benjy stared at him in surprise.

'Why – you're just like the picture of the little New Year I saw in the papers yesterday,' he said.

'I *am* the little New Year,' said the childlike creature. 'I'm young now – but if you saw me next Christmas you'd think I was as old as Santa Claus. It only takes twelve months for me to grow from a little New Year to a poor bent Old Year. Oh dear – to think of all the things that are going to happen in my twelve months!'

'Do you *know* what's going to happen, then?' asked Jennifer in surprise. 'Look – wrap this eiderdown round you. You'll be cold.'

'Oh no – I'm not cold,' said the little fellow, and he sat down at the end of the bed. 'Well – I don't know *exactly* what's going to happen – but I daresay my magic mirror does.'

'Magic mirror! Have you a magic mirror?' cried Benjy. 'Let me see it. What will it show me? All the things that will happen next year?'

'Perhaps,' said the little New Year. He took a small, round mirror from his clothes and held it up to the children. 'This is it. If you look into it, it will show you happenings in your New Year.'

'Oh – do let's look,' said Jennifer, and she peered into it excitedly. 'You look too, Benjy. We'll look together. Isn't it funny? It shines so brightly, and yet when we look into it it isn't like looking into a mirror – it's like looking through a window.' Jennifer gave a squeal.

'Oh, Benjy – I can see you in the mirror – you're sliding on the ice – oh, you've gone in – the ice is cracked and you've fallen in. Benjy, Benjy, what's happening to you?'

The picture faded away. Benjy looked worried. Another picture came. This time it was of Jennifer – and, oh dear, she was in bed with spots all over her face. She looked very miserable indeed.

'Oh, look – there's you, Jenny – and you're ill in bed with measles or something,' said Benjy. 'I don't like it.'

Another picture came – of Benjy and Jennifer together – and they were being chased by an angry man who looked like a farmer! Oh dear, this was worse and worse.

Other pictures came – of Benjy crying big tears, and holding a letter in his hand to say he hadn't passed the exam he so much wanted. And then there was one of Jenny in party clothes having her hand bandaged – and, oh dear, her lovely dress was scorched and burnt, and she was crying bitterly.

'Oh, don't show us any more,' she said. 'I can't bear it. All the pictures are terrible. Surely all those dreadful things aren't going to happen to us?'

'Well – they *may*,' said the little New Year. He had been watching the mirror too. 'They needn't, of course. It all depends on yourselves. For instance, Benjy certainly won't fall in the pond if he obeys his father and doesn't slide on the ice until he's told he can.'

'But what about me with measles?' asked Jenny.

'Ah, well – you'll be told not to go and play with a friend of yours who is ill,' said the New Year. 'If you do, you'll catch measles from her, no doubt about that – and into bed you'll go. And did you see that picture of you both being chased by a farmer? Well, you probably left his gates open or threw stones at his ducks – and that's why he's chasing you. If you're silly or unkind, that's what will happen!'

'I see,' said Benjy. 'And what about me howling because I didn't pass the exam? Aren't I going to pass it? I do so want to.'

'Well, you will if you work hard – but if you don't, that's a picture of yourself being sorry because you've been lazy and haven't passed it,' said the New Year.

'And the last picture – of me with my hand hurt, and my clothes all scorched and burnt,' said Jennifer, fearfully. 'What's happening there?'

'I expect you've played with matches and caught yourself on fire,' said the little New Year. 'It looks like it. But why do you look so worried? These things haven't happened yet!'

'But they're going to happen, aren't they?' said

Jenny, beginning to cry. 'They're in the mirror – and it's magic.'

'You're only looking at one side of the mirror!' said the little New Year, and he turned his mirror round so that the other side gleamed in front of them, clear and empty. 'Those are the horrid things that the year may hold for you. Here are some of the nice ones!'

The children watched as more pictures came – happy pictures of Jenny laughing and dancing at a party, of Benjy riding an elephant at the zoo, of them both winning prizes at school, of Benjy being clapped on the back because he had passed the exam ... much nicer pictures than the others!

'But – how can *both* these sets of things happen?' asked Jennifer, surprised. 'Benjy can't fail the exam and pass it too!'

'You're rather slow at understanding, aren't you?' said the little fellow, putting his mirror away again. 'Any of the things *might* happen, but whichever of them happens in the end depends on you and your behaviour now! Don't you *see*? If Benjy's lazy he won't pass the exam – if he works hard, he will. So either of the things may happen. It all depends on him. And if you disobey your mother and play with matches, you'll certainly get burnt. But if you are sensible, you will leave the matches alone – and instead of getting burnt you'll probably go to a party. Didn't you notice that it was a party dress in the picture that was scorched?'

'Yes, I did,' said Jennifer. She sat and thought for a long time. 'I understand what you mean now, little New Year,' she said at last. 'You mean that all sorts of things are going to happen – but we make them happen ourselves. Oh, I'm glad I've peeped into your magic mirror. Now I know what to do. But why don't you show everyone your mirror? Let them see the things that might happen, then everyone would be extra careful to do sensible, right things, and try to be good and generous.'

'I haven't time,' said the little New Year. 'Besides –

people wouldn't believe me. I'm glad *you* do. I think you'll have a happy New Year now!'

He slipped across to the window, climbed into the tree and slid down it. 'Goodbye,' he said. 'The noise has stopped. I must go and find the First of January!'

Off he went. The children lay down in bed, puzzled and wondering – and in the middle of their wondering they fell fast asleep, and didn't wake until the morning.

Mother came into the room. 'Wake up! Happy New Year to you both!' she said.

Jenny sat up. She looked across at Benjy. She remembered the strange visitor they had seen the night before. Or hadn't they? Was it a dream?

She called softly to Benjy. 'Benjy! Do you remember the magic mirror?'

'I shall never forget it,' said Benjy. 'Never. Jenny, let's tell everyone about it. People ought to know that it's themselves that make a year happy or sad.'

Yes, they ought to know it, and that's why I'm

telling it to you, so that you can make yours a happy one.

And what about Jenny and Benjy? Well, they are sensible children, so I don't think they will fall in an icy pond, get chased by a farmer, burn themselves, or fail exams – but if they do, I'll be sure to tell you.

Mr Stamp-About
Loses His Temper

Mr Stamp-About Loses His Temper

MR STAMP-ABOUT didn't like the snow. For one thing it made him walk slowly, and he didn't like that, because he liked to stamp about in a hurry. And for another thing the small boys always lay in wait for him, and threw snowballs at his big hat.

The worst of it was that they could run much faster than old Stamp-About, and by the time he had got the snow out of his collar, and picked up his hat again, there was never anyone to be seen!

'Wait till I catch you! Just wait!' stormed Mr Stamp-About, stamping in the snow till he had made it quite flat and slippery. But, of course, nobody ever did wait to be caught by Mr Stamp-About.

'The little wretches never knock off Mr Twiddle's hat,' he said. 'It's always mine! I'm always the one people play tricks on, and I don't like it. The very next time it happens I'll complain to Mr Plod the policeman. Yes, I will.'

So he did. A well-aimed snowball not only knocked off his hat, but the snow spread itself all over his face too, and he couldn't see anything for a minute or two. You can guess how he roared and stamped about! And off he went to find Mr Plod.

'I've been snowballed again!' he shouted at Mr Plod. 'My hat's a wreck! I've icy snow water all down my neck! Why don't you catch the little pests who do this to me? What's a policeman for, I'd like to know?'

'Now, now, Mr Stamp-About,' said Mr Plod. 'No need to shout at me. I'm not the one who played tricks on you. And how can I catch anyone if I don't know who they are? You don't even know their names to tell me.'

'How can I know them?' roared Stamp-About. 'They hide till I come – and then I'm so blinded by snow I can't see them.'

'If you could just *catch* one of them,' said Mr Plod, and Mr Stamp-About almost blew him over with his scornful snort.

'Pooh! Catch one! They're as slippery as eels. Aha – if ever I do I'll tie him up properly, and bring him to you, Mr Plod. And I hope you'll put him in prison.'

'Well, you bring him to me and I'll see,' said Mr Plod. 'Now, I've no more time to listen to you this morning, Mr Stamp-About, so don't begin all over again.'

Mr Stamp-About wasn't used to being spoken to like this, and he went purple in the face. But he couldn't say another word because Mr Plod picked up the telephone and began to have a very important conversation with the inspector. Mr Stamp-About really didn't dare to interrupt. So he went out, muttering angrily. If only he could catch somebody playing a trick on him!

Now, that evening Mr Stamp-About had to go and see his old friend, Mr Loud-Voice, who was ill with a cold, and was very upset because he had lost his voice. Mr Stamp-About stamped about his room, talking loudly, and poor Mr Loud-Voice was quite glad when at last he went.

It was when he was going home that things began to happen to Mr Stamp-About. He was walking along by Dame Old-One's house when suddenly something struck him.

It was snow! It struck Mr Stamp-About on the head, and quite knocked him over! He fell to the ground and the snow trickled down his neck in the horrible cold way it has.

Mr Stamp-About was looking for his hat when he was struck by something again – and once more he sank down under a mass of snow! He struggled up, and glared all around. Who was this, throwing enormous snowballs at him in the night? Who was it?

If only he could see them!

Aha! What was that? A figure hiding over there, at the corner? There was nobody else in sight. That was the wicked snowball-thrower! He thought Mr Stamp-About couldn't see him in the darkness, did he?

Mr Stamp-About didn't bother about his hat. Let it stay in the snow! He crept over the road, and then suddenly threw himself on the waiting figure, with a very fierce cry indeed. 'Got you! Got you at last!'

Down went his victim into the snow, his face buried in it so that he could only gasp and splutter. He began to struggle. He was big and strong, which did not surprise Mr Stamp-About at all. Anyone able to throw such enormous snowballs must certainly be very strong!

But Stamp-About was bigger and stronger. He soon managed to tie up arms and ankles with his tie and his belt. Then, because the fellow was heavy, he dumped him back in the snow and tied up his mouth with his handkerchief so that he couldn't call for help.

'And now,' said Mr Stamp-About to the struggling, trussed-up fellow, 'I'm off to the police station to get Mr Plod – and you'll soon find yourself spending the night in prison! Aha! I'll teach you to go about throwing snowballs at a person like me!'

Off he went. He soon arrived at the police station and shouted for Mr Plod. Mr Plod's assistant looked out of his room.

'Mr Plod's out on his rounds,' he said. 'Anything I can do?'

'I want you to come and arrest a fellow who's been lying in wait for me, and threw such enormous snowballs at me that I was completely buried under them,' said Mr Stamp-About, fiercely.

'Oh, I'll have to wait until Mr Plod comes back,' said the assistant. 'Can't leave the police station with nobody in it, you know. Where's this fellow?'

'Tied up at the corner,' said Stamp-About. 'You come along and take him to prison.'

'I tell you, we must wait till Mr Plod comes back,'

said the assistant. 'Anyway, if the fellow is all tied up he can wait. Do him good.'

So, very patiently indeed, Mr Stamp-About sat down and waited for Mr Plod. And Mr Plod didn't come. 'Must be on a case,' said the assistant. 'Burglary or something. Don't worry about the prisoner you've left out in the snow. I tell you it'll do him good to think about things a bit.'

'I daresay – but I want to get home to bed,' snapped Mr Stamp-About. 'It's cold in here. I'm getting tired of waiting.'

But still Mr Plod didn't come. And then at last, just as the police station clock was striking midnight, Mr Stamp-About heard voices.

'There's Mr Plod!' said the assistant, pleased. 'But doesn't he sound angry? I wonder what's happened.'

Mr Plod stalked into the police station, red with anger and shivering with cold. With him were two villagers, Old Man Wise and Father Wait-A-Bit.

'Sorry I'm so late,' he said to his gaping assistant.

'Some idiot leapt on me in the dark, got my face down in the snow and tied me up so that I couldn't shout or move! Wait till I get him. Just wait!'

'If I hadn't heard him muttering behind the hanky that was tied across his mouth he wouldn't have been found till morning,' said Old Man Wise.

'We just managed to untie him before he fainted with the cold,' said Father Wait-A-Bit. 'What a shocking thing it is that anyone should dare to attack and tie up our own policeman. The fellow must be punished!'

'And sent to prison for five years,' said Old Man Wise.

'No, twenty years!' raged Mr Plod, trying to get warm by the fire.

Now, Mr Stamp-About had been listening to all this in great surprise and horror. What – it was Mr Plod he had tied up – the policeman himself? Good gracious! What a truly terrible thing to have done!

Mr Stamp-About began to edge out of the room.

The assistant saw him. 'Oh, wait a minute – you wanted to ask . . .'

But Stamp-About no longer wanted to ask anyone anything. All he wanted was to get home to bed and hope that Mr Plod wouldn't hear anything about his waiting there all evening for him to arrest somebody that he, Stamp-About, had pounced on and tied up in the snow!

He went back home as quickly as he could. He suddenly remembered his hat. Where was it? Oh yes, he had left it buried in the snow by Dame Old-One's house! He had better go and get it.

He was fumbling in the snow there when suddenly he was struck down again. *Whoooosh!* Snow covered Stamp-About from head to foot! He sat down in a hurry, buried in snow.

What! Was there still someone about waiting to throw snowballs at him? No, it couldn't be. It must be – yes, it must be snow sliding off Dame Old-One's roof! It wasn't someone throwing enormous snowballs at him after all.

Whooooooooo ... began the snow on the roof again, and Stamp-About just skipped aside in time before another fall of snow crashed down. The snow everywhere was melting and here and there it was sliding off the steeper roofs, falling into gardens and on to pavements.

'I've been an idiot,' said Mr Stamp-About, as he hurried home. 'I thought a roof fall was a snowball – I pounced on Mr Plod thinking he was the one who had thrown the snow at me – and goodness knows what he'll do to me tomorrow when he hears all I've done. Prison for twenty years, he said. Well, I shouldn't be surprised!'

Poor Mr Stamp-About. He didn't go to sleep all night – and now it's morning and he's waiting to hear the footsteps of the policeman come plod-plod-plodding down the street. Well, well – unpleasant things always happen when people stamp about and lose their tempers!

Big-Foot Is Very Clever

Big-Foot Is Very
Clever

THE BROWNIE Big-Foot came knocking at the door of his friend's cave late one night. Little-Foot opened the door and peeped out.

'It's me, Big-Foot,' said the brownie. 'I've a most important letter here to be taken to old Mother Twinkle away on Breezy Hill.'

'Oh dear – and I've such a bad leg,' said Little-Foot. 'I can't walk all that way. You'll have to take it yourself, Big-Foot.'

'I can't. Breezy Hill is far from here and I have to get back early tomorrow morning because I have lots to do,' said Big-Foot. 'Get Swift-One the red fox to take it. He knows Breezy Hill very well.'

Big-Foot stayed the night. In the morning, what a surprise! The ground was covered with dazzling white snow!

'Look at that! I'll never be able to get to the fox's den through all the snow, with my bad leg,' said Little-Foot.

'Never mind. Maybe he has passed by here this morning,' said Big-Foot. 'I thought I heard him bark not long ago.'

'Well, we don't know which way he went!' said Little-Foot.

'*I* can tell you!' said Big-Foot. 'I can read footprints in the snow even if *you* can't!'

'How can you?' said Little-Foot, surprised.

'Well, just look here,' said Big-Foot, pointing to some tracks in the snow. 'I know that Hoppity the sparrow walked there – see his rows of little three-toed footprints set together in pairs – and, look, Web-Toe the duck walked there – you can see the mark of her webbed feet.'

'So you can,' said Little-Foot. 'And what are these bird prints? They're not in pairs like Hoppity's.'

'Oh, they probably belong to Freckles the thrush or Glossy the blackbird!' said Big-Foot. 'They are set one behind the other, see – not in pairs like the sparrow's.'

'This looks like a horse's big print,' said Little-Foot, getting interested. 'And this is a cow's, because the hoofprint is split in half, like the cow's foot.'

'Yes – and here's a cat's neat print,' said Big-Foot, 'and here's a dog's'.

'Surely you can't tell the difference!' said Little-Foot.

'I can. The cat draws her claws in when she walks, but the dog doesn't – so you can see the mark of his *claws* as well as the mark of his *paws*,' said Big-Foot. 'And – oh good – here's the print of the red fox!'

'It's just like a dog's! You can't tell it is the fox's

prints!' said Little-Foot disbelievingly.

'Oh, can't I?' said Big-Foot. 'Well, Swift-One has a bushy tail, hasn't he – and look, here and there are marks where it brushed against the snow! Those are the fox's prints, and if you follow them, Little-Foot, you'll find him, and you can give him the note for Mother Twinkle. Goodbye!'

Little-Foot set out after the fox, and followed his prints in the snow. He soon found him and gave him the note. Then he followed his own footprints back home!

Big-Foot was clever, wasn't he? See if you can be as clever when the snow is on the ground!

Two Good Turns

Two Good Turns

NEDDY WAS the little donkey belonging to Mr Johns. Sam was the little boy who lived at the greengrocer's shop and helped his father to weigh the potatoes, and set out the cabbages and apples in neat rows.

Neddy passed by the shop each day. Sam was always ready for him with a bit of carrot or half an apple.

'You spoil that donkey of Mr Johns',' grumbled his father. 'He's a lazy, stubborn little thing. Sometimes he stands still in the middle of the street and won't budge an inch.'

'Mr Johns isn't kind to him,' said Sam. 'He shouts

at him and beats him. If I were a donkey I'd stand still in the middle of the road sometimes, if my master was unkind to me.'

'Oh, you would, would you?' said his father. 'Well, you'd get beaten even harder if I were your master. Donkeys like that don't deserve kind words and pats. Now, you go and get on with your work. Fold up all those sacks and stack them neatly in the corner.'

Neddy came up the hill by the shop the next day, and Sam flew out to give him an apple.

But Mr Johns wouldn't let the donkey stop for it.

'He's been stubborn again!' he shouted angrily. 'Backed into a gate and broke a bit off the back of the car. He's not to have any treats. Come on, there! You bad fellow!'

Sam was sad. Neddy was sad too, because he did like an apple – and, more than that, he liked the loving words Sam spoke to him and the feel of Sam's hands on his neck. Ah, if only he had a master like that boy! He'd never be stubborn again.

The winter came. The weather grew colder and colder. Snow came, and it froze. More snow came, and that froze too, till the roads were as slippery as ice. Cars could no longer go up the hill by Sam's shop.

But the little grey donkey still came, sliding and slipping, pulling the heavy cart up the hill.

It's a shame, thought Sam, watching. *Poor little thing – it's terribly hard not to slip just here, where the hill is so steep. Neddy will break his legs one day!*

The next day the donkey stopped outside the shop. Mr Johns lashed him with the whip. 'Go on with you! What's the matter? You're the laziest animal there ever was.'

Neddy started off again, but his feet slipped all the time. Sam watched him, terrified that he would fall and break a leg. Mr Johns whipped him again.

Sam darted into the shop. He went to where the pile of sacks was, in a corner. He rushed out with them. He went to the donkey and flung a sack under his feet. Then he put another in front of him, and a third one higher up. He made a whole pathway of sacks – and the little donkey found firm footing on them and pulled the cart safely up the steepest bit. He looked round gratefully at Sam. 'Nice boy, kind boy!' his big donkey eyes said.

'He could have got up without all that,' shouted Mr Johns grumpily. 'Always making a fuss of Neddy! I tell you he's a lazy, stupid beast, and I'd be glad to get rid of him!'

Next day the frost was harder than ever. Sam was waiting with the sacks, and he made the same path for Neddy as the day before. The little donkey didn't slip at all. He was very pleased.

It was Wednesday and a half-holiday for Sam. What should he do? 'I think I'll go down to the pond, Dad,' he said. 'Not the one all the boys go to, because that's so crowded and I do want a good slide. I'll go to Bolter's Pond – that won't be crowded at all.'

He went to Bolter's Pond, and there were only two

boys on it, trying it. 'It's quite hard!' they yelled to Sam. 'Come and try.'

The boys soon left, and Sam thought he would have a really good, long slide. Soon he had a real beauty, and enjoyed himself immensely.

And then – and then there suddenly came a loud CRACK! And the ice split right across as Sam was sliding. He couldn't stop himself and slid straight into the crack, where the water was showing black below. In he went and gasped with the icy cold. He caught hold of the freezing edges of the ice and shouted loudly: 'Help! Help! Save me!'

But there was nobody near to hear, nobody at all. The boys had gone home. Bolter's Pond was in a lonely spot. 'Help! Help! Oh, save me!' cried poor Sam.

Somebody heard him then – somebody had been put into his shed a good distance away from the pond for the night. It was Neddy! He pricked up his long donkey ears when he heard the faraway voice calling.

Why, that sounded like Sam's voice! What was the

matter with him? The donkey stood and listened. He felt uneasy. Why was Sam calling?

Neddy knew how to undo his door, and he undid it now, jerking the catch up with his nose. He pushed the door and it opened. He galloped over the frosty hillside towards Sam's voice.

He was puzzled when he came to the pond. Sam's voice came from the middle of it! But he could only see Sam's head and shoulders. Why didn't the boy come to him as usual?

'Neddy! Oh, Neddy!' called Sam in a weak voice. 'I can't hold on much longer. Save me!'

But Neddy didn't dare to tread on the ice. He gave a frightened little bray and galloped away – away to the greengrocer's shop he knew so well. Where was Sam's father? He must come! He must come!

Sam's father was amazed to see Neddy walk right into his shop, and even more astonished when the donkey firmly caught hold of his sleeve and pulled him towards the door.

'Look, dear,' he cried to his wife, 'this donkey's mad! He's trying to take me somewhere.'

'Then, go, go!' cried his wife, suddenly feeling that something must be wrong. 'Go where he takes you!'

And Sam's father went with Neddy – down the hill, across the field to Bolter's Pond. And when he got there, he heard Sam's faint voice: 'Help! Help me!'

'Goodness me, it's Sam – gone through the ice!' cried his father and ran for a ladder. He brought one back quickly, laid it flat on the ice and pushed it towards Sam. The boy caught hold of the last rung and dragged himself feebly out of the icy-cold water. His father pulled the ladder to the bank and carried the boy home, the donkey following closely.

Sam caught a terrible cold and was in bed for two weeks. And every day, when Mr Johns passed by, he let the donkey look in at the bedroom window to see how Sam was getting on! Ah, Neddy was a hero now! He had had his picture in all the papers. '*Brave Donkey Saves His Little Friend!*'

And do you know what Sam's father is going to do? It's a secret, so don't tell Sam yet, if you should happen to know him. His father is going to buy Neddy and give him to Sam for his birthday! Won't Sam be pleased! 'Two such friends ought to be together,' says Sam's father.

And I think he's right – don't you?

Bad Luck,
Wily Weasel!

Bad Luck,
Wily Weasel!

ONCE BINKLE and Flip Bunny were walking home together through the snow, when they met Hasty Hare. He was lying in the snow, kicking up his legs and laughing till the tears ran down his whiskers.

'What's the joke?' asked Binkle Bunny.

Hasty sat up, still laughing. 'Well, you know old Wily Weasel?' he said. 'He's always chasing after us. I've just played a trick on him!'

'What did you do?' asked Flip.

'I got up on the roof of his house, which was piled high with snow,' said Hasty. 'And I waited there with a broom till he came out, then *whoooooooosh*!

I swept all the snow on to his head, and you should have heard him yell! I laughed so much that I fell off the roof on top of him.'

'He'll be after you then,' said Binkle, looking around in alarm, because he didn't like Wily Weasel at all.

'Oh, he thinks it was one of *you*,' said Hasty, with another giggle. 'I heard him yell out, "I can see you, Binkle – or is it Flip? One of you! I'll be after you both." Ho, ho, ho, really it *was* a joke!'

Hasty Hare loped off, still laughing. But Binkle and Flip weren't laughing at all. They looked at one another.

'It *was* a funny joke,' said Binkle, fearfully. 'But I do hope Wily didn't *really* think it was us!'

'Look – is that Wily coming – over there?' cried Flip, in great alarm. 'Run, Binkle, run!'

They ran – but Wily could run faster. He caught them up, and showed his sharp teeth. 'Oho! Now which one of you brushed that snow on to me?'

'Please – it wasn't us,' said Binkle. 'It was Hasty

Hare. Really it was. He just told us.'

'We've been to tea with Robert Rabbit,' said Flip. 'You can ask him. Call down his hole and see.'

Wily Weasel took them both firmly by the arm, and led them to Robert Rabbit's hole. He called down it. 'Hey, Robert Rabbit! You down there? Who came to tea with you today?'

'Binkle and Flip Bunny!' called back Robert. 'And what's it to do with you, I'd like to know?'

Wily Weasel didn't answer. He looked at Binkle and Flip out of his sharp eyes. He still held them tightly.

'Now you listen to me,' he said. 'I can't tell where Hasty Hare lives in all this snow. You know his house, and you're to take me to it – if you don't, I'll take *you* home for my dinner instead.'

'P-p-p-p-please let us g-g-g-g-go!' begged Binkle and Flip.

'Oh n-n-n-n-no!' said Wily, with a horrid smile. 'Come along, lead the way.'

Binkle mournfully began to lead the way, but to his surprise Flip pulled the other way. Binkle stared at him, and Flip gave a really enormous wink. Aha! Something was up. Binkle went the way that Flip was leading, wondering where they were going.

Across the snowy field. Up the snowdrifted lane. Past the white hedges. Up the white-blanketed hill. Then Wily Weasel began to grumble.

'It's a long way. I didn't know Hasty lived so far away. Are you sure you know where he lives?'

'Just wait and see,' said Flip. 'Look – do you see that gorse bush over there, covered in snow? Well, behind it you will see a small blue door.'

'Aha!' said Wily, snapping his teeth together. 'AHA! Hasty Hare, I'm coming. You just look out!'

'Now, you listen to what I say,' said Flip. 'You don't want to give him any warning, do you, that you're coming? Else he'll be out of his back door in a twinkling. You want to go – just – like – this . . .'

'On tippy – tippy – toe!' joined in Binkle, tiptoeing

on the snow. 'Sh! Then you want to give him an awful fright.'

'Yes, you should hammer on his door, and yell, "Where are you, you scoundrel?"' said Flip.

'And then you should fling the door open, stamp in and find him,' said Binkle. 'He'll probably be in bed – so you must rip the bedclothes off him . . .'

'And give him a box on the ear – *plonk!*' said Flip. 'That will teach him never, never to sweep snow off your roof again!'

'Right,' said Wily Weasel, and he began tiptoeing through the snow to the little blue door set in the hillside behind the gorse bush. When he got there he raised his fist.

Blam, blam, blam! He hammered on that door like thunder. Then he flung it open, crash! – and stamped into the little house. He came to a bedroom – and sure enough there was someone cuddled down in the bed.

Wily ripped off the bedclothes, and hit out with his

paw – biff! 'That will teach you to bury me in snow!' he shouted.

But oh my, oh my, what was this? It *wasn't* Hasty Hare asleep in bed. It was Snarl the Wolf! Wily stared down in the greatest alarm.

'*UrrrrrrRRRRRRRRR!*' growled Snarl, and leapt out of bed.

Outside the wolf's house, Binkle and Flip hid under the gorse bush and listened in fearful delight. Biff! Thud! Smackity-smackity! *UrrrrRRRRRRR.* Blam, slamity-slam, BIFF. Whatever could be going on there? How they longed to peep in and see – but they didn't dare even to show a whisker round the door.

And then Wily Weasel came flying out of the door, yelling loudly. He landed right in the middle of the gorse bush and yelled again. Then he made off home, limping and crying.

'*UrrrrrRRRRRRRRRR,*' said Snarl the Wolf, and slammed his door. Blam!

Binkle and Flip began to laugh. They rolled about under the bush till Binkle got badly pricked, and then they went home. Oh, what a joke to tell Hasty Hare!

And now Wily Weasel is looking for Binkle and Flip as well as Hasty Hare. But do you suppose he will find them? I don't think so!

I Dare You To!

I Dare You To!

IT WAS very cold weather. There was thick ice on the puddles. The village pond was frozen hard, and the ducks couldn't think what had happened to it.

'Can't we slide on the pond yet?' said Tom. His schoolteacher looked up.

'Not till I put the notice up,' he said. 'It isn't quite safe yet. Another night or two of frost and it will be all right. The ice isn't quite thick enough.'

'But, sir – we saw a couple of boys from the next village on it today,' said John. 'It seemed to be bearing all right.'

'I've nothing to do with the boys in the next village,'

said the master. 'I'm in charge of *you* – and I'm not running any risks of any of you falling in and drowning. I went on it myself this morning, and I heard it crack as I walked.'

The boys grumbled. Surely the ice was thick enough! Why, some of the big puddles were frozen solid – surely the ice on the pond must be almost solid too! The teacher couldn't have heard it crack that morning!

The boys all went home after school that day. They passed the pond on their way and looked at it longingly. Oh, for a slide on it! It was such a nice big pond. You could have a very fine slide indeed. Soon there would be skating.

'My uncle's given me a fine pair of skates,' said Tom. 'I shall go skating on Saturday – if only Mr Brown doesn't still think he hears the ice cracking!'

'I've got a toboggan,' said John. 'If there is snow on the hills, I shall go sledging. I shall have some fun, I can tell you!'

'My father's going to teach me how to skate properly,' said Tom. 'You'll soon see me gliding up and down at sixty miles an hour!'

'My mother's told me I can fetch my cousins on Saturday. They've got toboggans too,' said John. 'They will all come home to tea with me afterwards. My, we'll have sone fun!'

The two boys tapped the edge of the pond with their toes. It felt thick and solid. How they wished they could have just one slide! The other boys watched them tapping the ice with their toes and they tapped too.

'I say – look – there are the two big boys from the next village again!' said Tom, suddenly. 'Look – they're going on the ice!'

The two boys ran on the ice and began to slide up and down, up and down. The other boys watched them enviously.

'Hi! You know it's not supposed to be safe yet, don't you?' yelled Tom.

The boys slid up to them. 'What's not safe?' said one of them. 'Your pond? Pooh! It's as safe as can be. The ice is inches thick! Aren't you boys coming on for a slide?'

'No,' said Tom. 'We've been told it's not safe yet. We've got to wait.'

'Babies! Cowards!' said the boy, sliding off again. 'You're afraid, that's what's the matter with you! Cowardy-cowardy-custard!'

'We're jolly well not afraid!' yelled John angrily. 'It's like your cheek to say that – coming from another village and sliding on *our* pond! You wait till we're allowed on. We'll soon chase you off!'

'Come on and chase us off now!' mocked the two boys, sliding about. 'Come on!'

One of them slid near to Tom and John. 'I dare you to come on the ice!' he shouted. 'I dare you to!'

Tom and John hesitated.

'Babies! You're scared! I dare you to come!' yelled the boy.

'We can't be thought cowards, can we?' cried Tom, and he slid on to the ice. John followed. The two boys yelled rude things at them.

'Come on. After them!' shouted Tom. 'We'll show them if we're afraid or not! I always do what I'm dared to do!'

The other two boys set off to the further end of the pond. Tom and John followed them, close together. But just as they got to the middle, a horrible noise sounded.

'Crack-crack-crack-crack!'

It was the ice cracking. The weight of the two boys close together had been too much for it, for there was a thin place just there. An enormous crack had come, which widened quickly. Icy-blue water showed.

Tom was sliding and couldn't stop himself. He slid right into the crack, and fell into the water. Poor John followed him. They yelled as the cold water crept up to their waists.

'Help! Save us! Help!' they yelled in fright. They

clutched at the cold edge of the cracked ice, but it was so cold and slippery that they could not hold it.

The two boys from the next village took fright and fled away. The other boys, Tom's friends and John's, stared with frightened eyes.

'Fetch help!' yelled Tom. 'Quick! We'll drown!'

One of the boys darted off. He raced to the nearest house. There he found a sensible woman, who, carrying a long ladder, came as quickly as she could to the pond. She laid the ladder down flat on the ice, and it reached the two boys.

'Get hold! Clamber up!' she shouted. Tom managed to clutch the last rung. He turned and pulled John there too. The two boys were so icy cold that they could hardly use their hands.

But soon they were trying to clamber along the ladder that was lying flat over the icy pond. They reached the woman and she pulled them quickly to the bank.

'Silly boys! Going on the ice before it was fit

to bear!' she scolded. 'You'll catch your deaths of cold. Where do you live?'

'Not far off,' said Tom, whose teeth were chattering so much that he could hardly speak. 'We can run to our homes, both of us. Th-th-th-thank you for your h-h-h-help!'

Shivering with the cold, the two boys got to their homes as quickly as they could. Their mothers were shocked to see them so wet and so cold. Quickly they stripped off their dripping things, and bundled them into warm beds and gave them hot drinks.

But it was too late. The next day both Tom and John had terrible colds and coughs. They felt very ill. They didn't want anything to eat.

They were ill for three weeks. During that time the pond froze very hard, and people skated and slid all day long. The snow covered the hills too, and everyone went sledging and snowballing. The boys and girls at the village school had a wonderful time.

When Tom and John were better at last, and able to

go back to school, the snow had melted and the pond was water again, with ducks swimming gaily on it. The cold weather had gone for good – and the two boys had missed it all. How upset they were!

Their schoolmaster welcomed them back, but he didn't seem at all sorry for them when they grumbled that the cold weather had gone.

'You deserve to miss it,' he said. 'You were very disobedient.'

'Sir – we didn't mean to be,' said Tom. 'We were going to obey you, really we were – but the two boys from the next village called us cowards for not going on the pond.'

'Yes, sir – and they dared us to!' said John. 'They said, "We dare you to. Come on – we dare you to."'

'So we just had to go on, you see, sir,' said Tom. 'If they dared us, what else could we do? We had to be brave and show it.'

'Now look here,' said Mr Brown, 'let's get this silly "daring" business right. You were going to be loyal and obedient to my wishes – but someone else, that you don't know and don't care tuppence about, comes along and says, "I dare you to" – and you throw away all your loyalty and common sense, and do what they dare you to do, simply because you are afraid they will think you're cowards!'

The two boys looked at him. He went on, speaking in his low, even voice.

'You were so afraid they would think you afraid, that you let your fear of their scorn conquer you, and you did the silliest thing you could do – went on to a pond that didn't bear. Not very daring, Tom and John. The *really* brave thing would have been to say, "Think us cowards if you like – but we've promised not to go on, and we're not afraid of keeping our promise!"'

'Yes,' said Tom, suddenly seeing that Mr Brown was quite right. 'The thing we thought was brave, wasn't. It was just silly, done because we were dared to do it. The really brave thing would have been to laugh – and not to go out on the ice. I see, sir.'

'Good!' said his master. 'Three weeks in bed will be worth it, if you see the difference between a silly "dare", and loyalty to a promise. Well, I hope we get some cold weather again and we can send you off to slide and toboggan after all.'

But the cold weather didn't come again that year. It was a pity, because the two boys had to wait till the next winter!

The Hungry Little Robin

The Hungry Little Robin

FAR AWAY in the country, at the bottom of a big hill, there lived a little old lady all alone. Her name was Dame Twinkles, and it suited her, for when she smiled her eyes twinkled in her face.

She was a kind old woman, and although she was very poor, she always had a carrot to spare for the donkey in the field nearby, and a few crumbs for the birds.

One day, when it was winter, there came a spell of bitter, frosty weather. All the ponds and puddles froze up and even the little stream. The ground was so hard that it was like iron. The farmer took his donkey out of the field, and put him into a warm shed.

'Dear, dear!' said Dame Twinkles, looking out of her window. 'What bitter weather! How are the birds going to get worms out of the ground, or find any seeds, now everywhere is frozen hard? And where will they get water to drink?'

Outside there were some poor, cold little birds, wondering if Dame Twinkles was going to give them any crumbs. The thrushes and the blackbirds could not peck anything out of the hard ground. The robin could find no insects. The sparrows had eaten all the seeds and berries there were. Worst of all, there was no water to drink!

Dame Twinkles nodded at the little things. 'I'll bring you water in a minute,' she said. 'And I'll put out a few plant pots for you to roost in, with straw inside to keep you warm. And you shall have a fine cake all to yourselves!'

So she put out a big dish of water, and arranged some plant pots on their sides here and there, with straw inside. She knew that many birds would sleep in the pots that night, especially the little tits, who felt the cold so much.

Then she baked them a fine cake of different seeds and currants and flour, and put it on an old tree stump for them to eat. She cooked two large potatoes in their skins and split them open for the birds to peck at. She hung up a bone for the tits and the starlings. Weren't they delighted!

'Isn't she kind, isn't she kind?' sang the big blackbird.

'She's sweet, sweet, sweet!' sang the thrush.

'Shall I tell her, shall I tell her?' asked the robin in his creamy voice.

'Yes, do, yes do,' said all the birds. They knew that the robin was the tamest and friendliest of them all. So the little robin flew to the window and tapped on it with his beak. Dame Twinkles opened the window in surprise.

The robin hopped into the room, sat on the mantelpiece and sang with all his might to thank Dame

Twinkles. She listened and nodded.

'I understand you,' she said. 'I am glad to help you, hungry little robin! Come and peck at the window whenever you want anything.'

So after that, whenever he and the other birds were hungry, thirsty or cold, they sent the robin to peck at the window, and very soon he was so tame that he would perch on Dame Twinkles' shoulder and take crumbs from her mouth. She loved him, for he was a pretty, gay little thing with a beautiful voice.

One night that winter it began to snow. How it snowed! The flakes were as big as swan feathers, and they floated down all night long. The wind blew the snow against the little cottage at the foot of the hill and piled it up round it, so when Dame Twinkles awoke that morning she wondered why her cottage was so dark.

'Why, the snow is right up against my window!' she cried. 'I cannot see out! It must have been snowing all night long! I am snowed up!'

She dressed, and went to her front door. But she could not open it because of the weight of the snow against it. She was a prisoner!

'Good gracious!' said Dame Twinkles, afraid. 'What am I to do? I can't get out! Perhaps somebody will think of me, and come and dig me out.'

But nobody came. Nobody thought of the little cottage tucked away at the foot of the hill. All that day and the next night Dame Twinkles waited and waited – but nobody came to help her.

'If the snow does not melt, I shall starve here,' said the old lady to herself. 'It seems colder than ever. It might last for weeks!'

Now outside, the birds were wondering what had happened to the cottage, for it was half buried. On the second day, when no Dame Twinkles had appeared to give them food and water, the robin said he would try to find a window and peck at it.

So he scrambled through the snow and managed to make himself a passage to the window. He pecked on it.

'Tap-tap-tap!' Dame Twinkles jumped – then she saw that it was her hungry little robin. She opened the window and let him in. She gave him a few crumbs and a drink of water. He hopped on to her shoulder.

And then an idea came to Dame Twinkles. Suppose she wrote a tiny note, tied a piece of cotton to it, and bound it round the robin's leg, maybe someone would see it, and perhaps rescue her! So she quickly got a small piece of paper and wrote on it. She gently took the robin in her hand, and tied the little note round its leg.

'*Tirry-lee, tirry-lee!*' said the robin in surprise, but he did not struggle, for he was not afraid of Dame Twinkles.

'Listen, little friend,' said Dame Twinkles. 'Go to the farmer who lives on the other side of this hill, and let him take this note from your leg. I have been kind to you, and now it is right that you should do something for me.'

The robin carolled a little song and flew to the

window. He understood perfectly for he was very tame. He made his way through the snow, and flew up into the air. He sang to tell the other birds what he was going to do, and then he flew off to the farm.

The farmer's wife was a cheery, kindly soul, and was singing a little song in her kitchen when the robin tapped hard at her windowpane.

'Bless us all, it's a hungry little robin!' she said to the farmer, who was having his dinner. 'I'll let it in, and give it a bite to eat. Shoo, puss! Go into the hall or you'll frighten the robin!'

The cat shot into the hall. The door was shut on her. The farmer's wife opened the window and in came the robin. It flew to the table and sang to the farmer as loudly as it could.

'Well, here's a queer thing,' said the farmer, staring at the robin in surprise. 'What's it singing at me for?'

'It's got something wrong with its leg,' said his wife. 'Look – what's the matter with it?'

The farmer stretched out his hand, expecting the robin to fly at once, but it didn't. It stood there, half afraid, and let the farmer feel its leg.

'Why, it's paper,' said the farmer. He untied the note from the robin's leg and read it. 'Look, my dear, it's come from old Dame Twinkles to say she's snowed up, poor old thing. I must go and dig her out at once! Fancy her sending a letter by a robin!'

The farmer put on his hat and coat, took a spade, and went off through the snow to old Dame Twinkles. His strong arms soon dug away the snow from her door and windows, and made a good path for her to the gate.

'Oh, thank you, thank you!' cried the old lady. 'My little robin must have taken you the note very quickly!'

'He's a brave little thing!' said the farmer, looking at the robin, who was standing on the handle of his spade, flicking his wings. 'You're lucky, Dame Twinkles, to have a friend like that!'

'*Tirry-lee! We* are lucky to have a friend like Dame

Twinkles!' sang the robin. 'Are you all right now, Dame Twinkles?'

'Quite all right,' said the old lady, smiling. 'And tomorrow I will bake you all a fine new cake for yourselves for a treat!'

So she did – and last time I passed that way the birds were *so* busy eating it!

He Was Much Too Clever!

He Was Much
Too Clever!

THERE WAS once a rabbit who was very greedy. Nobody was pleased to see him popping in at teatime, for they knew that when he went, there wouldn't be a sandwich left on a plate or a bun in the tin.

'Hoppitty is such a greedy chap,' said the hedgehog. 'If ever I see him coming along *my* way I lock up my larder door at once.'

'And I put all my cakes into a tin marked "Tea" and hope he won't think of looking for them there,' said the squirrel.

So, very soon, Hoppitty found that it really wasn't much good popping in at teatime – for his friends never seemed to have anything to offer him. This upset him very much.

'If only somebody would give a party!' he said to himself. 'A real, good, old-fashioned party, with heaps of jellies and trifles and blancmanges and sandwiches and chocolate biscuits and lemonade! If only somebody would!'

One day Hoppitty mentioned his idea of a party to Brock the badger.

Brock was a kind and generous animal, and he really loved being friendly to everyone. He listened to everything that Hoppitty said, and nodded his striped head gravely.

'Why don't *you* give a party, Hoppitty, as you are so anxious to have one?' asked Brock.

'Well, you see, I'm very poor,' exclaimed Hoppitty. 'I'd *love* to give one, but it wouldn't be much of a party, I'm afraid, Brock – just a few grass sandwiches, that's all! Now if *you* gave a party – my word, how grand that would be! How people would love to come!'

'It *might* be a good idea,' said the badger, who loved having all his friends around him. 'Yes – I'll give one, Hoppitty. You shall make out the list of guests and write the invitations, for I'm no good at that sort of thing. I'll see to the food – you see to the other part.'

Hoppitty was delighted – especially as a very clever idea had come into his long-eared head!

'Now just suppose I ask all those animals who go to sleep for the winter!' he said to himself. 'They won't be able to come to the party, of course – so when I arrive I'll be the only guest, for *I* don't sleep in the cold weather. And I can eat everything! My word, that *is* a good idea!'

He did a little jig of joy as he thought of it. Then he sat down to think again. 'Whom shall I ask?' he said. 'Well now, Prickles the hedgehog sleeps in the wintertime, so I'll ask him. And Dozy the dormouse does too – and so does Flitter the bat. That's three. Then there's Bushy the red squirrel. He's nearly always asleep in the wintertime. And Slither the snake too. I found him asleep in the hollow tree last winter, so I know he doesn't like the cold weather. Oh, and Croak the frog and Crawler the toad, of course! They sleep soundly in the wintertime!'

Very soon Hoppitty had sent out the invitations for the seven guests. He told Brock about them – but he didn't tell the badger that each of the guests would be fast asleep by the time the party day came! Oh no – Hoppitty was really being very clever.

'Well, they sound all right,' said Brock, pleased. 'With ourselves, that makes nine. A very nice number for a party. And here is the list of things we're going to eat, Hoppitty.'

He handed Hoppitty a list. The rabbit's eyes nearly fell out of his head as he read it.

'Twenty radish sandwiches. Twenty lettuce sandwiches. Twenty tomato rolls. Six chocolate blancmanges. Six trifles. Six pink jellies. Six yellow jellies. Two pounds of chocolate biscuits. Six jugs of sweet lemonade.'

'Oh, fine, fine!' said Hoppitty. 'This will be the best party ever given in Bluebell Wood, Brock. You are really most generous. Now, what about the date? I think the first of November would be a good time.'

'Very well,' said Brock, who hadn't much idea of time. 'I've got a calendar on the wall of my den. I tear a day off each morning. I shall know when November the first is coming near. You can depend on me.'

All the guests answered their invitations, and they all said they would come. Hoppitty grinned when he read the letters.

'They will all be fast asleep for the winter!' he chuckled. 'None of them will be able to come then – and I shall have the finest feast I've ever had. Brock will eat a few of the things, I dare say – but I'll eat the most.'

Hoppitty could hardly wait till November the first. Frosts came in October, and the animals shivered. The last swallows left. The leaves fell, and a good many of the smaller animals began to feel very sleepy.

The hedgehog found a hole in a bank, lined it with moss and dead leaves, and fell fast asleep. The dormouse slept in a cosy hold underneath a treeroot. The snake found a hollow tree and coiled up there with its brothers. The toad slept soundly under a big mossy stone, and the frog went down to the mud at the bottom of the pond. The squirrel decided to take a nap too, till a warm spell came, and the bat shivered and went to hang himself upside down in an old barn he knew.

November the first came at last – a fine, cold day with a round, red sun in the sky. Hoppitty was tremendously excited. His sister had knitted him a new blue scarf to wear for the party, so he really looked very smart.

'I'll try and bring you home a lettuce sandwich,' he promised her. 'Now, it's four o'clock – I must be off. My, there *will* be a spread in Brock's den!'

He sped off, chuckling to think that all the other guests were fast asleep. How silly they were –

and how clever he was!

He came to Brock's hole. It was blocked up, but there was a bell pull outside. Hoppitty rang it and heard the bell jangling loudly. Nobody came to open the hole.

Hoppitty rang again. Still there was no answer. The rabbit was puzzled and cross. This was November the first – and Brock should have got everything ready! Wherever was he?

'Brock!' shouted Hoppitty. 'Do come and open the door! It's me! Hurry, because it's cold standing out here.'

There was no answer at all. Hoppitty began to pull at the bracken that was stuffing up the hole, but it was so firmly wedged in that he couldn't move it.

'I say, Brock!' he called, drumming on the ground with his hind feet. 'Come at once!'

A thin red nose poked out of a hole nearby, and Rufus the fox looked at Hoppitty with a sly grin.

'Why do you want Brock?' he asked.

'Because he's giving a party today,' said Hoppitty, rather scared of the fox. 'I can't think why he doesn't come to the door!'

'But *I* can,' said Rufus slyly. 'He's asleep.'

'Asleep!' cried Hoppitty. 'You don't really mean that?'

'Of course I do,' said the fox. 'Don't you know that badgers sleep in the wintertime, the same as hedgehogs and dormice and snakes? Brock stuffed up his hole two weeks ago, and he and his family are snoring away deep down at the bottom. I know, because I've heard them. There won't be any party today.'

'Oh dear!' wailed Hoppitty in despair. 'And I did so want a really good tea. I'm terribly hungry.'

'So am I!' said Rufus the fox, coming out of his hole. 'I want a really good tea too – a rabbit tea!'

He shot after the frightened bunny, who ran for his life. He was very nearly caught, for the ends of his new blue scarf flew out behind him and the fox caught one of them in his teeth. But the scarf tore in half, and

Hoppitty just managed to run down his burrow in time, startling his sister almost out of her skin when he rushed full tilt into her.

He told her all about the party, and how he had had such a good idea, asking guests that he knew couldn't come.

'But I didn't think that Brock the badger would be asleep too,' he said sadly.

'The trouble with you is that you're much too greedy and think yourself too clever,' said his sister, who was cross about his torn scarf. 'I'm glad this has happened. Perhaps it will teach you a lesson.'

'It will,' said Hoppitty mournfully. 'I'll never do such a thing again!'

Mr Pink-Whistle Comes Along

Mr Pink-Whistle Comes Along

'SOOTY!' CALLED Mr Pink-Whistle to his big black cat. 'I'm going for a walk. It's a lovely sunny winter's day. I'll be back in time for lunch.'

Sooty went to the door to see him off. He went briskly down the garden path and out of the gate. The frost crunched under his feet as he went, and the pale December sun shone down on him. What a lovely day!

I think I'll go down to the pond to see if there are any children sliding on the ice, he thought. So off he went, down the lane, up the hill, down the hill, and across a meadow where frost whitened the long grass in the ditches.

Mr Pink-Whistle was just putting his leg over the stile to go to the pond when his sharp ears heard a sound. He had pointed brownie ears and could hear like a hare!

Now, what's that? he thought, a leg half over the stile. *Is it an animal? Or a child? Or just a noise?*

It seemed to come from a little tumble-down shed by the hedge. Mr Pink-Whistle listened. Yes, there certainly was a noise – a sniffy sort of noise: sniff-sniff-gulp, sniff-sniff!'

'I'd better go and find out,' said Pink-Whistle, and he got down from the stile and went to the little shed. He poked his head inside. It was rather dark and he couldn't see anything at first. Then he saw something white. 'Dear me!' said Pink-Whistle. 'Is that a face I see? Does it belong to someone? Who are you?'

The face was peeping out of a pile of hay in the corner of the shed.

'Yes, but please go away. This is my shed. It's private.'

Pink-Whistle didn't go away. He was sure that he could see the face was very miserable. He came right into the shed.

Somebody scrambled out of the hay crossly. It was a boy of about ten. 'I told you this was *my* shed,' he said. 'It's on my father's land and he said I could have it for my own. You're trespassing!'

'Was it you I heard sniff-sniff-sniffing?' asked Pink-Whistle. 'What's the matter?'

'Nothing,' said the boy. 'Nothing to do with you anyway. Don't you know when people want to be alone? I wish you'd get out of my shed.'

'I'm going,' said Pink-Whistle. 'But it's a pity you haven't even a dog to keep you company. If you're unhappy, it's nice to have a dog's nose on the knee.'

He walked back to the door. 'Come back,' said the boy suddenly, sitting down on the hay and rubbing a very dirty hand over his face. 'I like what you said just now. You might understand if I tell you something. You wouldn't have said that if you hadn't understood what friends dogs are, would you?'

'No,' said Pink-Whistle, turning back. 'So it's something to do with a dog, is it? Your own dog, I suppose.'

'Yes,' said the boy in a shaky sort of voice. 'You see, I've got no brothers or sisters, so my dad gave me a dog for my own. My very own, you understand – not one that's shared by the whole family. Buddy was my own, every whisker of him, every hair.'

'That's a splendid thing,' said Pink-Whistle. 'I expect you belonged to him as much as he belonged to you. You were his friend as much as he was yours.'

'I'm glad you understand,' said the boy. 'It's nice to tell somebody. Well, Buddy's gone. Somebody's stolen him. He was a black spaniel with big, loving eyes, and he cost my father a lot of money. That's why he's been stolen, because he's valuable.'

Sniff-sniff-sniff! The boy rubbed his hand over his eyes again. 'I'm ten,' he said, ashamed, 'and too old to make a fuss like this, like a four-year-old. I know all that, so you needn't tell me. But a dog sort of gets right into your heart if he's your own.'

'I shall begin to sniff too, in a minute,' said Pink-Whistle. 'I know exactly what you feel. You're thinking how miserable your dog will be without you, and you're hoping that nobody is being cruel to him, and you're wondering if he's cowering down in some corner, puzzled and frightened. Well, that's enough to make anyone feel miserable.'

'He disappeared yesterday,' said the boy. 'Two men came to the farm to ask if they could buy chickens – and I'm sure they took Buddy away. They may have given him some meat with a sleeping powder in it and got him like that. The police say they can't trace the men and they haven't had any report of a black spaniel anywhere.'

'I see,' said Pink-Whistle. 'Er – do you happen to know me by any chance, young lad?'

'My name's Robin,' said the boy. 'No, I don't know you. I've never ever seen you before, have I?'

He peered closely at Pink-Whistle. The sun shone in at the little shed window just then and he suddenly saw Pink-Whistle clearly. He saw his green eyes and pointed ears and he gave a little cry.

'Wait! Wait! Yes, I've seen your picture somewhere in a magazine or a book. Yes, I remember now. Why – surely you're not Mr Pink-Whistle?'

'I am,' said Pink-Whistle, beaming all over his face, pleased that the boy knew him. 'And I like to go about the world putting wrong things right.'

'Get back Buddy for me then, please, please, please!' said Robin, clutching hold of Mr Pink-Whistle's arm. 'I never thought you were real, but you are. Can you get back Buddy?'

'I'll do my best,' said Pink-Whistle. 'I'll go now. Cheer up, get out of this dark shed and go home and find some work to do. Perhaps I can put things right for you.'

He walked out of the shed. Robin ran after him, suddenly very cheerful indeed. He was amazed. To think that Mr Pink-Whistle should come along just then – what a wonderful thing!

Pink-Whistle went back home. He called Sooty, his cat, and told her about Robin. 'Go to the farm and speak to the farm cats,' he said. 'They will have noticed these two men and have seen if Buddy was taken away by them. Find out all you can.'

Sooty ran off, tail in the air. She soon came back with the news. 'Yes, master! The farm cats say that the men came back that evening, threw down meat for Buddy and then went away. Buddy ate it and fell asleep. Then the men came back and put him into a sack. The cats heard them saying they were going to Ringdown Market on Thursday. You will find them there.'

'Thank you, Sooty!' said Pink-Whistle. 'That's all I want to know.'

The next Thursday, Pink-Whistle set off to Ringdown Market. It was a long way away, but he got there at last. What a babble of sound there was! Horses whinnying, sheep baaing, hens clucking, ducks quacking, turkeys gobbling, geese hissing and cackling!

Pink-Whistle looked for a black spaniel. There were three for sale at the market. Which was Robin's? Mr Pink-Whistle decided to make himself invisible. This was a gift he sometimes used, and he used it now!

One moment there was a kindly old man walking about – the next moment he wasn't there at all! An old woman selling eggs was most astonished. She blinked her eyes in wonder and then forgot about it. Pink-Whistle went up to a black spaniel. 'Buddy!' he whispered. 'Buddy!'

The dog took no notice. So that one wasn't Robin's dog. Pink-Whistle went up to the second spaniel and whispered. But he wasn't Robin's dog either.

'Buddy!' whispered Pink-Whistle to the third spaniel, who was lying miserably on some sacks behind two men selling hens. 'Buddy!'

The dog sprang up at once, his tail wagging. He looked all around. Who had called him by his name?

One of the men turned round sharply.

'Lie down, you!' he shouted. Pink-Whistle felt very angry indeed. Aha! These fellows wanted punishing. They wanted frightening. Well, he would have a grand game and give them a wonderful punishment.

He began to bark like a dog and Buddy pricked up his ears at once. Then Pink-Whistle pretended that Buddy was speaking.

'Hens, peck these men!' he cried. And then it seemed to the men as if a whole flock of invisible hens were all around them, pecking hard – but really, of course, it was Mr Pink-Whistle jabbing at them with his hard little forefinger – peck-peck-peck!

The men cowered back, squealing. Everyone came to see what the matter was. Pink-Whistle called out again in a barking sort of voice, so that it seemed as if Buddy was talking. 'Geese, attack these men!'

And dear me, what a cackling there was from old Pink-Whistle then, what a hissing – and what a jab-jab-jabbing from top to bottom of the scared men. Everyone stared, amazed. What was happening? Where did the cackling and hissing come from? Who was jabbing the men?

'Serves them right,' said somebody. 'I never did like those two.'

And then Pink-Whistle decided to be a butting goat! What fun he was having – and what a wonderful punishment he was giving the two men!

'Goat, butt them!' he cried. The men looked everywhere, scared, wondering if an invisible goat was coming at them.

Biff! Pink-Whistle ran first at one man and then the other. Biff! Bang! Biff! The men felt exactly as though a big, rather solid goat was butting them back and front. Pink-Whistle butted one man right over and he rolled on top of Buddy. Buddy promptly snapped at him and growled.

Pink-Whistle immediately growled too, and talking in his growling voice, said, 'Bull, toss these men!'

The men gave a loud howl. Hens had pecked them, geese had jabbed them, a goat had butted them! Surely, surely they were not going to be tossed by a bull, and an invisible one too, coming at them from any side!

'Run for it!' yelled one man, and he ran for his life. The other followed. Pink-Whistle galloped after them, making his feet sound like a bull's hooves – clippitty-clippitty-clop. How the men howled!

Pink-Whistle couldn't follow them very far because he was laughing so much. How he laughed! People were really puzzled to hear loud chuckles and not to see anyone there.

'Well, I don't know what's upset those two fellows,' said a burly farmer, 'but I'm glad to see the back of them. Rascals, both of them!'

Pink-Whistle went back to where the dog Buddy lay on the sacks, puzzled and frightened. Buddy suddenly heard a quiet, kindly voice talking to him, and invisible fingers undid the knot of rope that tied him to a rail.

'Come with me, Buddy,' said the voice, and Buddy went obediently. He sniffed at Mr Pink-Whistle's invisible legs. How very peculiar to smell legs that didn't seem to be there! Buddy couldn't understand it – but then, he didn't really understand anything that had happened since he had left Robin. His world seemed quite upside down and not at all a nice place.

It was a long way to the farm where Robin lived – but as they got nearer to it Buddy became very excited indeed. His nose twitched. He pulled against the hand on his collar.

'Not so fast, Buddy,' said Mr Pink-Whistle. 'I want to come with you.'

Buddy took another sniff at the invisible legs. Well, they smelt all right, so the person with them ought to be all right too. He trotted along obediently, getting more and more excited.

It was dark when at last they came to the farm. Buddy pulled and pulled at Pink-Whistle's hand. The little man led him to his kennel. 'Get in there and wait!' he ordered. 'And bark. Bark loudly!'

Buddy crept in and then he barked. How loudly he barked. 'Wuff-wuff-wuff, WUFF-WUFF. Robin, I'm back, where are you? WUFF-WUFF!'

And Robin heard of course. He would know Buddy's bark anywhere! He sprang up at once, his face shining. 'Mother! That's Buddy's bark! He's back!' he cried and raced out of the house to the yard. He came to the kennel, calling joyfully, 'Buddy! Buddy! I'm here!'

And, before Buddy could squeeze past the invisible Mr Pink-Whistle, there was Robin, squeezing into the kennel! He got right in, and then you really couldn't tell which was boy and which was dog, they hugged and licked and rolled and patted, and yelped and shouted so joyfully together!

At last, tired out, they sat peacefully together in the kennel, Buddy's nose on Robin's knee and Robin's arm round Buddy's neck. Only Buddy's tongue was busy, lick-lick-licking at Robin's hand.

'Buddy, I do wish I could say a big thank you to Mr Pink-Whistle!' said Robin. 'I don't even know where he lives, though. I'd say, Mr Pink-Whistle, I'm your friend for ever and ever!'

Pink-Whistle heard it all. He was peering in at the kennel, as happy as could be. He had put a lot of things right in his life, but surely this was one of the very best! He stole away in the darkness, a very happy little man indeed.

She Never Could
Remember

She Never Could Remember

'I'M HOME, Mummy!' called Pam, flying into the sitting room and flinging her schoolbag on the table. 'What's for lunch?'

'Something nice,' said Mother. 'Hang up your hat and coat and scarf. Where are your gloves? Your hands are cold.'

'Oh, in my pocket, I expect!' said Pam. She felt there and then in the other pocket. But they weren't there.

'Pam! You haven't lost them again, have you?' said her mother, vexed. 'It's really too bad of you. That's the third pair this month.'

'Oh dear – I can't think how it is they disappear

like that,' said Pam.

'Now listen,' said Mother. 'I shall sew a little button in each of your pockets, and sew a tape to each of your gloves. And at the other end of the tape I shall make a buttonhole, so that you can button your gloves into your pocket! Then they won't be lost.'

'But the tape will show, Mummy – coming out of my pocket to my gloves,' said Pam.

'Yes, it will,' said Mother. 'But it can't be helped. I'm not going to have you losing a fourth pair of gloves. Now go and hang up your things.'

Pam's mother did as she said. She sewed little buttons inside Pam's coat pockets, buttoned a length of tape on to them, and sewed the gloves to the end of the tape. Now, even if Pam forgot to put them into her pocket, it didn't matter – they would hang safely down on the tapes!

Well, Pam went off to school that afternoon feeling cross. She knew the other children would tease her about the gloves on tapes, and they did. She sulked all the way home and stamped crossly into the house.

'Wipe your feet!' called her mother. 'They must be very dirty on a day like this. Well – what about your gloves? Did you bring them back safely this time?'

'Yes, Mummy,' said Pam, sulkily. 'They're on my hands, look. I kept them on all the way home. You needn't have taped them on like that. Everyone laughed at me.'

'Well, you shouldn't have been so careless, dear,' said her mother. 'Now hang up your things. Where's your scarf?'

Would you believe it, Pam hadn't got her scarf! There was her hat – there was her coat – and her gloves, of course – but no scarf! 'I must have left it at school,' she said in a small voice.

'There now!' said her mother. 'That shows how careless you are, doesn't it! Go back at once and get it.'

Pam ran back and halfway there she found it lying by the roadside in the mud. Oh dear! It must have fallen off without her knowing it. She ran back quickly, wanting her tea.

'I hadn't left it at school,' she said. 'It just dropped off, that's all. Here it is. A bit muddy, I'm afraid.'

Her mother looked at it grimly. 'A bit muddy! It's black! Very well, Pam, when it's washed and dry you can wear it again but I shall pin it to your coat in future – then it can't drop off again.'

'Oh, Mummy! I can't go to school with taped gloves and a pinned-on scarf!' wailed Pam. But it wasn't a bit of good talking to her mother like that. If her mother said a thing, she meant it.

So next day off went Pam to school with her gloves taped to her pockets and her scarf pinned to her coat. It was a very warm day and she puffed and panted. How she wished she could take off her scarf, but she didn't dare to unpin it.

It was such a lovely day that the teacher let all the children out early. 'Go and play in the field,' said Miss Brown. 'You've all worked hard this morning, and you deserve a little extra play.'

So out they all went into the field. 'Let's play rounders,' said John. 'Come on, pick sides.'

So they picked sides and then began to play. But before two minutes had gone by they were all much too hot.

'Gracious! We'll have to take off our hats and coats,' said Kenneth. 'Pile them over there, on this old tree stump.'

So coats and hats were quickly thrown over the old stump and the children began to play again. It was fun in the warm autumn sun.

A bell rang suddenly. It was from the school. 'That's for the bus children!' cried John. 'My word – is that the bus coming now? We'll have to hurry!'

All the bus children snatched up hats and coats and ran for the bus. Pam didn't have to catch the bus, so she didn't go with them, but she suddenly remembered something.

Gracious! Mummy told me to be sure and come home early today because we're going to see Granny's new house! she thought. *And it's later than usual now. I must run!*

She ran to the gate, slipped through it and rushed home. She quite forgot her coat and other things. She was so warm that she didn't miss them at all.

She ran in, panting. Mother was in the kitchen serving up the lunch. She called to Pam.

'Pam, it's late, dear. Take off your things quickly and wash your hands. Bring me your gloves to let me see if they are clean enough to go to Granny's in.'

Pam looked at her hands but, of course, she had no gloves on. Oh dear – were they in her pocket then? She couldn't have lost them because they were buttoned into each pocket!

She had no pockets – because she had no coat! She stood still, quite bewildered. She put her hand up to her neck. No scarf either! Oh goodness, what had happened?

Her mother came in, carrying a hot dish. She looked at Pam. 'Did you hear me say I wanted to look at your gloves?' she said. 'Where are they – in your coat pocket? My word, you have got your things off quickly!'

'Mummy,' said Pam, her face bright red, 'I haven't got my gloves – or my scarf. I – I—'

'What do you mean?' said her mother, putting the dish down. 'I pinned your scarf to your coat and buttoned your gloves into your pockets. Don't be silly.'

Pam didn't know what to say. She was wondering about her things. Could she really have come home without them?

'Don't stand there staring, child!' said her mother sharply. 'Lunch is waiting and we've got a bus to catch. Fetch your coat and get your gloves out of the pockets.'

'Mummy, I haven't got my coat. I – well, I forgot it,' said Pam. 'And my hat too.'

Her mother stared at her in amazement. 'Pam! You forgot your coat – with the scarf and gloves fastened to it – and your hat too? How could you have forgotten them?'

'We all went to play rounders in the field and we

were too hot, so we took off our things, and when I ran home – because I was late – I left them behind,' said poor Pam, all in a rush.

'Well you'll just have to go and get them then,' said her mother. 'And either you will have to go without your lunch or I shall have to go to Granny's without you. What am I to do with you? Shall I pin your hat to your head and your coat to your back?'

Pam ran off, crying. She was ashamed and upset. Now she knew how careless she was! To think she could leave everything behind!

She ran to the field. She went to the old tree stump but it was empty except for green ivy leaves growing all over it. Not a single coat or hat was left there!

Pam looked in horror. Someone must have come along and stolen it. Whatever would Mummy say now? It was a new school coat, only bought that term. Had she enough money in her moneybox to buy another?

Perhaps somebody found my things and took them to the

police station, thought Pam, at last. *People are supposed to take anything they find to the police. I'll go and ask.*

She was rather scared of going to the police station, but she did so hope to find her things there, so up the steps she went and walked timidly into the room where two policemen sat busily writing. They were surprised to see Pam.

Pam stammered out what she had come for. 'Please – has somebody brought my things?' she said.

The bigger policeman of the two shook his head. 'No. Nothing's been brought in, miss. We'll let you know if they are. My word, that was a careless thing to do, wasn't it – to leave the whole lot behind!'

'And you've got to remember something else, miss,' said the other policeman solemnly. 'Supposing we find that a tramp has stolen them, or somebody else that came by, and we catch him. You wouldn't like to think somebody had been sent to prison because you'd been careless enough to leave your clothes for him to steal, would you?'

This was a most alarming thought. Pam wouldn't say a word. She went home very sad indeed. As she went down the road the bus passed her – and there was Mummy in it! She had waited and waited for Pam, and hadn't been able to wait any longer.

Pam was so upset that she went down into the back garden, sat in the fork of the old apple tree, and cried. She'd lost her lunch and lost the treat of going to see Granny's new house – besides losing her clothes as well. She stayed out in the garden for a long time, miserable and cross with herself. Then she felt cold and went slowly indoors. A smell of burning came to her nose.

She ran into the kitchen. Oh dear, oh dear! Mummy had left her lunch warming up in the oven, and everything in the dish was frizzled brown! To think she could have had her lunch after all!

Then she caught sight of something very peculiar indeed – something that made her stare and stare.

Her hat and coat were hanging on their usual peg!

Her scarf was there too – and her gloves peeped out of the pockets! What a very, very strange thing!

Did I come home in them after all? Pam thought. *Did I? I must have done. Oh, how forgetful I am! No wonder Mummy gets so cross with me. Whatever can I do to show her I'm not as bad as she thinks?*

Well, you should have seen how busy Pam was after that. She took down her mother's sewing basket and mended every pair of socks there – and mended them well too. She went to her mother's linen basket and pulled out hankies and vests and a blouse of her own and she washed them beautifully! Out on the line they all went.

Then she went to look in the shed. There was her father's bicycle, and her mother's too, both rather dirty. She got cloths and dusters and she cleaned those two bicycles till they shone!

She was very hungry, because she had had no lunch. Should she get herself some tea? It was very late now – about half past five. How she wished she had been to

Granny's and had one of Granny's glorious teas – a large slice of real chocolate cake, egg sandwiches, homemade ginger biscuits, and perhaps a warm jam tart! It made her feel very hungry to think of such a good tea.

She heard somebody coming in at the front door. Could it possibly be her mother, coming home so early? She flew out to see – and it was!

'I came home early because I knew you'd be all alone,' said Mother. 'I passed you in the bus. Did you see me?'

'Yes, Mummy!' said Pam. 'I was awfully silly – I went down to the garden and cried and when I got back to the house the lunch that you left was all frizzled up, so I couldn't eat it. But, Mummy, I must have come home in my things after all, because – look, they're hanging on their usual peg!'

'Yes, I know,' said Mother. 'I put them there. Kind little Jane brought them home for you – and you'd just gone off to find them! You didn't hear me calling you back. Why were you gone so long?'

Pam told her about the police station. 'I'm glad nobody stole my things,' she said, feeling happier. 'I wouldn't like to feel that somebody was in prison for stealing just because I was careless enough to leave my things in the field for them to take!'

'What's that washing on the line?' said Mother suddenly, seeing it out of the window.

'Oh, I did want to show you I'm not as bad as you think, Mummy,' said Pam, 'so I did your bits of washing and I mended the socks – and I've cleaned the bicycles!'

'Well! Now I know you're better than I ever imagined!' said Mother, pleased. 'And look what I've brought you from Granny!'

She opened a big paper bag and set out egg sandwiches on the table, six ginger biscuits, a most enormous slice of chocolate cake, and two little jam tarts.

'Dear old Granny sent them for you,' she said.

'I said no, I wasn't going to take anything home to such a careless, naughty girl, but Granny said I might find a good one when I got in – and she was right!'

Pam was so pleased. She sat down and began to eat hungrily. 'Listen, Mummy,' she said, when she had finished. 'You don't need to pin my scarf on any more, or tape my gloves to my pockets. I've turned over a new leaf – a huge new leaf – and you can trust me now!'

And her mother at once unpinned the scarf and snipped the tape of the gloves. Wasn't that nice of her? She felt sure that Pam was telling the truth.

She was, of course. She's the most dependable little girl you ever saw now!

The Swallow Fairy

The Swallow Fairy

ONCE THERE was a small fairy who played all summer long with the swallows. She had long curved wings as they had, and she flashed in the air with them, racing them over the fields and back.

They lived on the insects they caught in the air. The swallow fairy lived on the honey she found in the flowers. The bees and butterflies showed her how to get it with a long, very tiny spoon.

'We have a tongue to put into the flowers, to suck out the honey,' they said, 'but you haven't a long enough one. So use a spoon.'

Now, in October, a cold wind blew. The swallow

fairy shivered. There were not so many flowers with honey in and she was sometimes hungry.

There were not so many insects flying in the air either, so the swallows were often hungry. And when the cold wind blew, they gathered together on the roofs of the barns and on the telegraph wires, chattering and twittering.

The little martins were there with the swallows too. They were cousins of the swallows and loved to fly with them high in the sky. 'Don't let's stay here in this cold wind!' they cried. 'Let's fly off to a warmer country.'

'Yes, do let's!' said the swallows. 'In a warmer country there will be more insects. There are so few here now. We will go!'

'Oh, don't leave me!' cried the swallow fairy. 'I shall be so lonely. Take me with you.'

'It's too far for you to fly,' said her best friend, a fine long-tailed swallow with a shining steel-blue back. 'You would fall into the sea and be drowned.'

'Oh, will you fly across the sea?' said the fairy. 'I shouldn't like that. I'll stay here – but will you come back again?'

'In the springtime,' said the swallow, and then suddenly, almost as if one of them had given a signal, the whole twittering flock flew into the air and wheeled away to the south. They were gone. Not one was left.

The fairy was lonely. She sat crying in the evening wind, sitting on a barn roof by herself. A little black bat saw her and flew near.

'Come and live with me!' he cried. 'Do come!' So the fairy went to live with him. But as the wind grew colder he wouldn't go out to fly. He hung himself upside down in an old cave, with hundreds of others like himself. And he went to sleep!

'Wake up, wake up!' cried the fairy. 'You're a dull sort of friend to have, little bat!'

'Leave me alone,' said the bat sleepily. 'I'm too cold to fly. I shall sleep till the sun comes again in the spring. Hang yourself upside down, fairy, and sleep too.'

'I don't like hanging upside down,' said the fairy. 'I don't like hanging myself up at all. And I don't like this cave either. It smells.'

'Well, go and live with someone else then,' said the bat in a huff, and wouldn't say another word.

The fairy flew off. She came to a pond and sat by it, feeling cold and lonely. A frog was there, talking to a fat, squat toad. 'Hallo, fairy!' said the frog. 'Why do you look so miserable?'

'I'm lonely,' said the fairy. 'I've no friend to live with.'

'You'd better tuck yourself away somewhere for the winter,' said the frog. 'Come with me and I'll keep you close to me, little fairy.'

'All right,' said the fairy. 'Where are you going?'

'I'm going down into the mud at the bottom of the pond,' said the frog. 'I shall sleep there all winter. It's a nice cosy place to sleep.'

'Oh, I'd *hate* that!' said the fairy and shivered. 'Cold and muddy and wet! I'd rather go with the toad. I always did like his lovely brown eyes.'

'Yes, you come with me,' said the toad, and took her to a big stone. Underneath was a fine hiding place, just big enough for the fairy and himself. He dragged her underneath with him. Then he shut his eyes. The fairy went to sleep too. But she soon awoke and shivered.

'This is a nasty damp place,' she said. 'I shall get a cold. Toad, let's go somewhere else.'

But the toad was fast asleep and wouldn't answer. So the fairy left him in disgust. She walked fast to keep herself warm – and she ran into a hedgehog, also hurrying fast. He carried a leaf in his mouth.

'Oh, hallo!' said the fairy. 'Where are you off to, with that leaf?'

'I've got a cosy little house in a warm bank,' said the hedgehog. 'I'm lining it with leaves. Why don't you come and live with me there? It's really a very nice little home, with a curtain of moss for a door.'

'All right, I'll come,' said the fairy, who thought the hedgehog's home sounded nice too, all lined with dry dead leaves, and quite warm.

But the hedgehog was so prickly that the fairy couldn't possibly cuddle up to him. And whenever he moved, his prickles stuck into her. That wasn't at all nice.

'I'll have to go,' said the fairy. 'I'm sorry, but you're not very cuddly, hedgehog.'

The hedgehog said nothing. He was fast asleep. He wouldn't wake up for weeks!

'This is very boring,' said the fairy to herself, scrambling out of the warm hole. 'All my friends seem either to be flying off to warmer lands, or finding places to sleep away the winter. I don't want to do either – but yet I *must* find somewhere for a home. And I'd dearly like to have a nice friend I could talk to too – not one who's going to snore all winter long.'

She met a snake and he invited her to go to a hollow tree he knew and curl up with him and all his friends together. 'We knot ourselves together for warmth,' he said. 'It's a very nice tree we go to, fairy. Do come.'

'Well – no thank you,' said the fairy. 'I like snakes and I think they're very clever the way they glide along without feet – but I don't want to be knotted up with you all winter. I might want to get out and not be able to, because I'm sure you'd be fast asleep.'

'Oh, we should,' said the snake. 'Well, what about trying the dormouse? He's a nice cosy fellow, and he would keep you warm and not mind a bit if you wriggled in and out of his hole during the winter. He's in the ditch over there.'

The dormouse was very fat. He told the fairy that as he never had anything to eat all the winter, he liked to get as nice and fat as possible before he went to sleep.

'Don't you ever wake up in the winter?' said the fairy. 'I really do want a cosy, furry friend like you to cuddle up to – but it's so dull having a friend who is asleep all the time and never says a word. And oh dear

– I don't know *what* I shall do for food soon. There isn't any honey to be found at all, except in a few odd flowers here and there.'

The dormouse went close to her and whispered, 'I know where there is a store of nuts. Do you like nuts?'

'Oh, yes,' said the fairy. 'Very much.'

'Well, do you see that clump of ivy over there?' asked the dormouse, pointing with his tiny foot. 'I happen to know there are about a dozen nuts there. You could feast on those.'

'Oh, thank you,' said the fairy. She watched the dormouse go down to his little hole in some tree roots. She liked him very much – but he *would* be dull as a friend, because she knew what a sleepy fellow he was.

She flew to the ivy and found the nuts. She was just wondering how to crack one when she heard scampering feet, and a cross voice: 'Hey! Don't you take my nuts!'

'Oh – are they yours? I'm so sorry,' said the fairy,

and put the nut back quickly. She looked at the animal beside her. She liked him very much. He was a red squirrel, with bright eyes and a very bushy tail.

The squirrel looked at the fairy, and he liked her too. He was suddenly sorry he had been cross, because the fairy looked cold and hungry and lonely. He took up a nut. 'Would you like me to give you one?' he said. 'I don't like people to steal them, but I never mind giving them away.'

He gnawed through the shell, and got out the nut. He gave it to the fairy. 'Oh, thank you,' she said, and began to nibble it.

'You seem very hungry,' said the squirrel. 'Where is your home?'

'I haven't one,' said the fairy, and she told him how she had tried to find someone to live with in warmth and friendliness. 'You see – so many creatures go to sleep all the winter – and that's dull, isn't it?'

'Very dull,' agreed the squirrel. 'I think what *I* do is much more sensible. I sleep in my cosy hole when the weather is very bitter, with my tail wrapped round me for a rug – and when a warm spell comes, I wake up, scamper down my tree and find my nuts to have a feast. I have a good play, and then when the frosty night comes again, I pop back to sleep.'

'That does sound a good idea,' said the fairy. 'Sleep the coldest days away – wake up in the sunshine and play, and have a good meal – and go back again when the frost nips your toes. You're the most sensible of all creatures I know, squirrel. How I wish you were my friend!'

'I'd like to be,' said the squirrel. 'You come with me to my hole and sleep with me wrapped up in my tail. And perhaps, in the springtime, when I want to go and find a nice little wife, you'd brush and comb my fur well and make me beautiful.'

'Oh, I *will*!' said the fairy. 'I'd love to do that. Red Squirrel, let's go to your hole now – I'm cold.'

So up the tree they went and the squirrel curled up in his hole with the fairy beside him. He wrapped his bushy tail round them both and they slept cosily together.

And when a warm spell comes they both wake up and look for the squirrel's nuts. So if you ever see a red squirrel scampering in the winter sunshine, look around and see if you can spy his small companion hiding anywhere.

You *might* see her. You never know!

Father Time and
His Pattern Book

Father Time and
His Pattern Book

ONE NEW Year's Eve, in the middle of the night, Robin woke with a jump. He sat up in bed and listened. Whatever could have wakened him?

Then he heard slow footsteps outside his window, and he wondered who it could be wandering around in the garden in the middle of the night!

Perhaps it is someone who is lost in the snow, he thought. So he jumped out of bed and went to the window. He opened it and leant out. It was dark outside but he could just make out something moving below.

'Who's there?' he called, and a most surprising

answer came up to him.

'I'm Old Father Time! I've come to collect this year's patterns.'

'This year's patterns! Whatever do you mean?' said Robin in astonishment. 'And what are you doing in our garden?'

'Well, I came to collect your pattern too,' said the old man.

'I haven't got a pattern!' said Robin. 'You must be dreaming.'

'Maybe I am,' said Father Time. 'But my dreams are true ones. It's cold out here, little boy. Let me in and I will show you some of my patterns.'

'I think the dining room should still be warm,' said Robin, excited. 'I'll let you in, and we can go into the dining room for a bit. Shall I wake Mummy?'

'Oh no,' said Father Time. 'Don't wake anyone. Hurry up and let me in.'

Robin slipped downstairs. He opened the front door quietly and someone came in. Robin went to the dining room and switched on the light. Then he saw his visitor for the first time.

Father Time was an old, old man. His beard almost reached the ground. He had a wise and kindly face, with dreamy, happy eyes and a sad mouth. He carried a great scythe with him, which Robin was most surprised to see.

'What's that for?' he asked. 'Did you get it out of our garden shed? It's what we use to cut the long grass.'

'This scythe is mine,' said Father Time. 'I use it to cut away the years from one another. I cut time with it.'

'How strange!' said Robin, feeling excited. 'Now, do show me the patterns you spoke about! Where are they? And what are they?'

Father Time didn't have any book of patterns. Robin had thought he would have one rather like the book of patterns that Mother sometimes got from the man who sold curtains. But except for his scythe he had nothing at all.

'My patterns?' he said. 'Oh, I have them all, though

you can't see them just at the moment. Everyone makes a pattern of his life, you know. Your brother does. Your friends do. I'll show you any pattern, you like to ask me for.'

'Well, I'd like to see what pattern my brother made last year,' said Robin.

Father Time put down his scythe carefully. He put out the light. Then he held up his hands in the darkness and from the fingers of Old Father Time there flowed a shining ribbon, broad and quivering as if it were alive. It was as wide as the table, and it flowed down on to it like a cloth, spreading itself flat for Robin to see.

'I say! It's a lovely pattern,' said Robin. 'I shouldn't have thought my little brother could have made such a beauty. How did he make it?'

'The pattern is made of the stuff he put into each day,' said Father Time. 'The happy moments – the times he ran to do a kindness – the times he cried with fear or pain. They are all in the pattern.

This line of silver is a line of love – he loves very much for it is a beautiful line. This glowing thread shows his happy times – he is a happy little boy. This shimmering piece is a great kindness he did, about the middle of the year. It shines because it shines in everyone's memory.'

'Yes, I remember that,' said Robin. 'I hurt my leg and couldn't go to a party. So Lenny wouldn't go either and he brought me every single one of his toys and gave me them for my own, because he was so sorry for me – even his best railway train that he loves. I shall never forget how kind he was to me. But what is this ugly little line of black dots that keeps showing in the pattern?'

'Those spots come into a pattern when the maker of the pattern loses his temper,' said Father Time. 'He must be careful, or as the years go on the spots will get bigger and bigger and spoil his pattern altogether.'

'Oh dear, I'll have to warm him,' said Robin. 'Now show me Harry's pattern, Father Time. You know –

Harry Jones. He lives next door. Have you got his for last year?'

'Yes, I collected it tonight,' said Father Time. The pattern he had been showing Robin faded away into the darkness, and from Father Time's fingers flowed another one that spread itself on the table as the others had done. It was an ugly pattern, with two or three bright threads lighting it up. Robin looked at it.

'It's not a very beautiful pattern, is it?' he asked.

'No. Harry cannot have done very well with his three hundred and sixty-five days last year,' said Father Time sadly. 'See – that horrid mess there means greediness and selfishness – and here it is again – and again – spoiling the pattern that the bright threads are trying to make.'

'Yes, Harry is selfish,' said Robin. 'He's an only child, and thinks everything must be for him. What are the bright threads, Father Time?'

Father Time looked at them closely. 'They are fine, strong bits of pattern,' he said. 'They are hard work that Harry has done. He is a good worker, and if he goes on trying hard, those bright threads will be so strong that they will run right through those messy bits. Maybe one day he will make a better pattern.'

The pattern faded. Robin thought for a moment, and then he asked for another. 'Show me Elsa's, please,' he said. 'She's such a nice girl. I like her.'

Once again a pattern flowed over the table. It was a brilliant one, beautiful and even. It would have been perfect except that it seemed to be torn here and there.

'It's lovely except for those torn bits,' said Robin.

'Yes – Elsa must be a happy and clever girl,' said Father Time. 'But alas – look at these places where the pattern is quite spoilt! That means cruelty, Robin – a thing that tears the pattern of our lives to bits. Poor Elsa! She must be careful, or one day her pattern will be torn to pieces, and all her happiness will go.'

'How strange, Father Time!' said Robin, astonished. 'That's one thing I can't stand about Elsa – she is so unkind to animals. I've often seen her throw stones at them. And yet she's so nice in every other way.'

'Tell her about her pattern,' said Father Time. 'For maybe one day a moment of cruelty will spoil a whole year and more.'

'Now show me Leslie's pattern,' said Robin. 'He's such a funny little boy, Father Time – so shy and timid, like a mouse! I'd love to see the kind of pattern that he has made this last year.'

Once again a pattern flowed in the darkness – but what a strange one! It could hardly be seen. There was no brightness in it, no real pattern to see. It was just a smudge of dingy colours.

'Poor little boy!' said Father Time. 'He is afraid of everything! He has put no brightness into his pattern, no happy moments, no kindness – only shyness and fear. Robin, you must help him to make a better pattern next year. Tell him to have courage and not to be afraid of doing kindness to anyone. Then his pattern will glow and shine.'

The pattern faded. Father Time went to switch on the light. 'I must go,' he said. 'I have many other patterns to collect tonight and put into my book of history.'

'Wait a minute!' said Robin. 'Please, Father Time – may I see my own pattern?'

'Yes, you may,' said Father Time. He didn't put on the light, but held up his strange fingers once again. And from them flowed the pattern of all the days of the last year – the pattern made by Robin himself.

Robin looked at it, half fearful, half excited, wondering what he would see. He saw a brilliant pattern, full of bright colours that danced and shone. In it were pools of silvery light, but here and there were smudges of grey that spoilt the lovely pattern he had made.

'Ah, Robin, you have done well this year to make such a fine pattern,' said Father Time, pleased. 'You have been happy, for see how the pattern glows. You have worked hard, for see how strong the pattern is, unbroken and steady. You have been kind, for here are the silver pools that shine in the pattern and shine in your friends' memories too.'

'But, Father Time – what are those grey smudges that spoil the pattern here and there?' asked Robin, puzzled. 'I don't like them.'

'Neither do I,' said Father Time. 'They show where you spoilt your days by telling untruths, Robin. Truth always shines out in a pattern, but untruths smudge it with grey. See – you did not tell the truth there – and there – and there – and look, as the pattern reaches the end of the year, the grey smudges get worse. You have let that bad habit grow on you and spoil the lovely pattern you were making.'

'Yes,' said Robin, ashamed. 'I have been getting worse about telling untruths, I know. Mummy keeps telling me that. I didn't know they would spoil the pattern of my year, though. I'll be very, very careful next year – I shan't tell a single untruth, then my pattern will be really lovely.'

'Be careful nothing else creeps in to spoil it,' said Father Time. 'I will come next year and show you the pattern you have made. Now, goodbye – I must go. I feel much warmer and I have enjoyed our talk!'

'So have I! It was wonderful,' said Robin. 'Thank you very much, Father Time!'

The old man slipped out of the house and Robin went back to bed. He dreamt all night long of the year's patterns, and when he woke in the morning he couldn't think whether it had all been a dream or not.

'Anyway, I shall know next New Year's Eve,' said Robin. 'I shall look out for the old man again then – and see the pattern I have made. I do hope it's beautiful.'

Would you like to see the one you made last year? What do you think it would be like? I would love to know.

Mr Snoop's Carrots

Mr Snoop's Carrots

ONE DARK, cold winter the village of Shiver was hungry – so hungry that some of the people began to look very thin.

'Our potatoes have gone bad,' they said to one another. 'The harvest was poor too, so we have very little corn to make bread. It's no good asking the next villages to help us, for they are as badly off as we are.'

'We had better all bring what we have got to the mayor,' said Dame Bent. 'Some of us have turnips and carrots, some have corn, some have dried meat. Let us all bring what we have got, and then the mayor can share it out between us so that we all have the same.'

'Yes, that is a good idea,' said Mother Bright-Eyes. 'It will be fair to everyone.'

Old Man Snoop didn't think it was a good idea at all. He had a whole cellarful of carrots, good orange carrots, and he didn't want to share them with anybody. There were enough there to make him soup for the whole winter. Why should he share them with anyone else?

Everyone had to go to the mayor and declare what he had in his cellars or larder. Then, the next day, the mayor would send men to collect the things, and after that they would be stored and doled out through the cold, hungry winter.

Mr Snoop went to declare what stores he had. 'A dozen carrots,' he said in a doleful voice, 'and a packet of tea, a little sugar, and a little dried meat.'

'Why, Mr Snoop, you have hundreds and hundreds of carrots,' said Dame Bent, at once. 'You know you have! Surely you are not thinking of keeping those for yourself? A dozen carrots, indeed! I hope the mayor's servants will explore your cellars well and take away all your carrots! You're a nasty, mean old man.'

'I am not!' said Mr Snoop, feeling angry because everyone had heard what Dame Bent had said. 'I have only about a dozen carrots, as I said, and the mayor's servants can certainly explore my cellars! And, to prove that I am not mean, I say this – I will only take from the mayor exactly half the food he gives to others. So there!'

There was a silence after these words. People didn't know what to think. Could Mr Snoop have a cellar full of carrots if he was willing to let others look and see? And could he be so mean as they thought if he offered to take only half the food that everyone else was having?

'Well, we'll see what we shall see,' said Dame Bent, and she turned away. She told the mayor to be sure to tell his servants to look at Old Man Snoop's cellars carefully next day for she did not trust him at all.

Old Man Snoop went home very angry. Now,

because of that interfering Dame Bent he would have to hide all the carrots he had stored in his cellar!

'I'll put them into my barrow and wheel them to the middle of Long Field, and dig a hole there and bury them,' said Mr Snoop to himself. 'I'll hide them all away and only leave about a dozen in the cellar. I shall be able to slip out each night and get some in for my soup – so I shall easily be able to manage on half the food that the mayor gives to the others. Ha! They thought I was generous over that!'

That night, Old Man Snoop wheeled many barrow-loads of carrots to the middle of Long Field. He dug a big hole and buried them there. Then he marked the place with four white stones set together.

The next day, the servants of the mayor came round to everyone to collect what food they had. They came to Old Man Snoop's house and asked for the food he had in his larder and cellars. He flung open the doors.

'There you are!' he said. 'Take what you see. I don't wish to keep anything back.'

There were only a dozen carrots in the cellar! 'He told the truth,' whispered one servant to another. 'Dame Bent was wrong.'

The next day everyone went to the storehouse to get their ration of food – Old Man Snoop too. He asked for only half, for he had made up his mind to appear very good and generous. 'And don't give me any carrots, please, because I don't like them at all,' said Mr Snoop in a loud voice, hoping that Dame Bent would hear him. 'They give me a dreadful pain. On no account give me carrots.'

He knew he would have plenty of carrots of his own to eat! Clever Mr Snoop!

That night Snoop went to fetch himself a few carrots for soup, and he had a very good meal, far bigger than anyone else in Shiver Village. He went to bed and slept soundly, for his meanness never worried him.

In the morning, what a surprise! The ground was deep in snow! It was still snowing when Mr Snoop looked out of the window, and it snowed all day.

Well, that was the end of Mr Snoop going out to find his carrots! The four white stones that marked them were buried deep under the snow. He couldn't go digging down all over the field, for people would see the marks in the snow and guess what he had been doing. It was most annoying.

So Mr Snoop had to go without his carrots, and as he had only half the amount of food that everyone else had, he felt very hungry. What a mistake he had made!

'Never mind,' he said to himself. 'When the snow goes I shall find my carrots again, and I shall be all right. I must go hungry for a few days.'

During the snow the rabbits in the fields were very hungry too, for the grass was buried under the snow. But soon a rabbit smelt the pit of carrots, and it wasn't long before he had dug a tunnel to them, and told all his brothers and sisters about them.

The rabbits had a wonderful time eating the carrots; and then one morning Dame Bent, walking down the snowy path that ran round Long Field, noticed a bitten carrot lying on the snow. Then she saw another, and another. She followed them and came to a big hole in the snow leading down to the pit of carrots, which was now uncovered by the rabbits.

'Look at that!' said Dame Bent, guessing that it was Old Man Snoop's hoard of carrots. 'I must tell the mayor, and he must send his men to collect such a lovely store of carrots. My, my, my!'

Well, the carrots were soon collected, but Old Man Snoop didn't know that. He didn't get any of them, of course, because he had said that he didn't like carrots. He was very glad when the snow went, because now, he thought, he could go out and fetch in plenty of carrots from his store. And how hungry he was!

So, that night, when the weather had turned warm, and all the snow was melting, Old Man Snoop took his lamp and went out with a basket to find the four white stones that marked his pit of carrots.

But there were no carrots there except for a few

half-eaten ones that were hardly any good at all. Old Man Snoop stood there and wept.

'Oh, my carrots! Oh, my lovely carrots! The rabbits have got them. Oh, what a dreadful thing!'

The next day, Mr Snoop went to the storehouse with the others to collect his food ration, and he saw piles and piles of carrots. Dame Bent saw him looking at them and smiled.

'Ah, Mr Snoop, what a pity you don't like carrots,' she said. 'These were found most unexpectedly in the middle of the field by your house. Extraordinary, wasn't it? Everyone is getting a good share of them each day except you; and, of course, you don't like carrots.'

So poor Mr Snoop had to go without his carrots, after all; and, as he only had half the food that other people had, he felt very hungry and miserable indeed all that winter.

How glad he was when the cold weather went and springtime came, with its new stocks of green food and salad and rhubarb. How he gobbled everything up!

I'll never be so mean again, he thought, as he sat down to a rhubarb pie. *I'm so thin that my bones rattle against one another, and all because I was mean and greedy, and wouldn't share with others. I don't think I deserved to lose all my carrots like that, all the same.*

But he did, of course; and it was a very good thing too, that he lost them, because it cured him of some very nasty ways, didn't it?

A Jolly Thing
to Do!

A Jolly Thing
to Do!

'MUMMY, WILL you read to us after tea?' asked Peter.

'I can't, darling. The cold I've got has given me a sore throat and made my voice go croaky,' said his mother. 'I'll play with you, if you like.'

'I don't want a game,' said Jean. 'If you can't read to us I want to make something, Mummy. Can't we make something?'

'Yes, if you like,' said her mother, and she thought hard. 'Listen, if you'd like to go out into the wood this afternoon, while I have a rest, and bring back whatever you find, we'll make something that you can take to school with you tomorrow!'

'Oh, Mummy, what?' asked Peter.

But she shook her head and laughed. 'How can I tell you what we shall make until I know what you will bring back?' she said.

'But, Mummy, it's November, and there's hardly anything to find in the woods,' said Jean. 'No flowers, no anything.'

'Well, if you can't bring back anything, we can't make anything,' said her mother. 'You must see what you can find, even if it's only a few twigs!'

That afternoon, when their mother had gone to have a rest, Peter and Jean put on their coats and wellington boots, took a basket, and went out. They walked down the lane to the woods and shuffled through the dead leaves that lay thick on the ground. Peter saw a fir cone and picked it up.

'Look,' he said, 'here's something – a nice dry cone.'

'We can't make much with that!' said Jean. 'But cones burn nicely on the fire. We could take some home for that, if you like.'

So they filled their basket with cones, big and small. Then they came to a little thicket of oak trees. There were still some old brown leaves on the trees, rustling in the wind.

'We might find some acorns underneath,' said Jean. 'Let's look.'

So they hunted about and found quite a lot. 'They're nice,' said Jean, 'so smooth and oval. I like them. We could give them to the pigs at the farm, if we can't make anything with them. And here are some acorn cups too, Peter.'

'What are those brown balls on the oak trees?' said Peter, and he pointed to where hard round balls, like brown marbles, grew here and there on the bare branches of the oak.

'Those are oak apples,' said Jean. 'I learnt about them in school this term. They're called galls. They're not the fruit of the oak, Peter – they're just growths caused by insects.'

'How strange,' said Peter, and he picked some off

the twigs. 'They look exactly as if they might be the fruit of the oak – though I know those are acorns. We'll take some of these home too, shall we, Jean?'

So into their basket went the oak apples and rattled there with the acorns and cones.

Then Jean found some red haws on the bare hawthorn tree. 'Look!' she cried. 'Do you remember the white may blossom we saw here in the summer? Wasn't it lovely? Now the fruit has come and it's these round red berries the birds like so much. Shall we take some sprays home with us? They're so pretty.'

'We'll take some twigs too,' said Peter, and he broke some here and there from the trees. 'We can put them into a vase if we don't use them.'

'It looks as if it's going to rain,' said Jean, looking up at the sky. 'We'd better get back quickly before we're soaked.'

'But we haven't many things to take home,' said Peter. 'What can Mummy make with these? Nothing much!'

'I expect she'll be able to,' said Jean. 'I felt a drop of rain then. Come on, Peter, before it pours down.'

They ran home and got in just before the storm broke. They emptied their basket on to the kitchen table and then took off their coats and boots. It wasn't quite teatime, so they took their books and read. They didn't want to make a noise because their mother was still having her rest.

At teatime they showed her what they had brought home from the woods.

'Not very much, Mummy,' said Jean. 'But really there wasn't much to find. In summer there would be heaps of things.'

Mother looked at their collection of fir cones, acorns, oak apples and the rest.

'Quite a nice lot of things!' she said. 'We shall be able to make some fir cone girls! They are easy to make and look comical when they're done.'

'Oh, let's start quickly!' said Jean, who loved making things. 'Mummy, how do you make them?'

'Finish your tea first,' said their mother, so both children hurried up and finished it. Then they went to the table where they had put their things. Mother gave them a large sheet of newspaper to spread over the table so that they wouldn't make too much mess.

'Now,' she said, picking up a fir cone, 'this shall be the fir cone girl's dress. It looks nice and frilly, doesn't it?'

So it did! Then she picked up a brown oak apple. 'This shall be her head,' she said. 'Have you got your paintboxes out, children? You can paint white eyes, a white nose and a white mouth on the dark oak apple, for a face.'

Peter and Jean chose a nice round oak apple each. Soon they were busy painting funny little faces on them.

'Mine's finished,' said Jean, holding hers up. 'She's smiling.'

'Good,' said Mother. 'Now we'll stick the head firmly on to the bottom bit of the cone – where the stalk is. Your stalk is too long, Peter. Cut it off till it's level with the bottom of the fir cone.'

'How do we put the head on firmly?' asked Peter.

'We can glue it on,' said his mother. 'Or, if you like, you can bore a hole in the neck of the fir cone, and a little hole under the chin of your oak apple face, and put a bit of matchstick into the holes to hold them together, so that the oak apple is joined very firmly indeed to the cone. Put a spot of glue where they join as well.'

Peter managed to put his oak apple head on the fir cone body by means of a bit of match driven into the little holes he made, but Jean glued hers on without bothering about holes or matchstick.

'Now we've got body and head,' said Mother. 'What about legs and arms?'

'Twigs, of course,' said Peter, and he began to break one up into bits for arms and legs.

'Make a little forked bit come just where the hands should be,' said Mother. 'It looks more real then.

Now, you can stick them on with glue, if you like, or bore holes in the twigs and the cone and join them with pins or bits of matchstick – whichever you like.'

The children worked hard. Soon they had legs and arms finished.

'I wish mine would stand up,' said Jean.

'We'll make stands for our fir cone girls then,' said her mother, and she fetched an old cork from the cupboard. She cut three pieces from it. 'There,' she said, 'now we have stands for our girls. Bore holes in your bits of cork, and then stick the twig legs into the holes, dabbing a spot of glue where they meet.'

Peter managed his beautifully, but Jean broke one of the legs, and had to get another bit of twig.

'That's right, Jean,' said her mother. 'You've got a fine little twig, this time, with a bent bit that looks like a knee. Now put it very carefully into the cork.'

'Our fir cone girls have got dresses, arms, legs, heads and faces,' said Peter, 'and something to stand on. What about hats?'

'Oh, these acorn cups would do for hats!' cried Jean, and she rummaged about in the acorns for the little cups some of them had been in. 'Look, Mummy, aren't these cups pretty, with their tiny stalks? They look as if someone had carved a pattern all round them.'

Jean stuck an acorn cup over the oak apple head. It fitted beautifully.

'My fir cone girl looks very smart,' she said. 'Try one of yours, Peter. Here's a nice one.'

'I want mine to have hair first,' said Peter. 'I don't want her to be bald. Mummy, what can I have for hair?'

'Well, you try and think of something yourself,' said his mother. Peter looked all around. He saw some yellow wool in the workbasket – just the thing for hair!

'Can I have some of that yellow wool?' he asked. 'I could snip short bits off and glue them on my doll's oak apple head.'

'Yes, you can both have some of the wool if you like,' said Mother. But Jean didn't want yellow wool. She thought she would have black wool. Soon both children were neatly snipping short bits from the wool. Then they glued them on to the dolls' heads.

'Now to put on their acorn hats!' cried Jean, and popped hers on. The dolls looked very good. The children were delighted!

Jean saw the red hawthorn berries she had brought home with her. 'They'll do for buttons down her dress,' she said, and dabbed glue down the front of the fir cone frills. She squeezed the berries on, and they looked like red buttons.

'Mine won't have buttons,' said Peter. 'I'll run a little ribbon under the scales of the cone round the middle and make a sash for my fir cone girl.'

They were finished. Mother and Peter and Jean stood them up on the mantelpiece and smiled to see the funny fir cone girls there.

'Mine's called Fanny Fir Cone,' said Jean.

'Mine's Alice Acorn,' said Peter.

'And mine's Olive Oak Apple,' said their mother. Then they all laughed.

'You must take them to school with you tomorrow,' said Mother, 'and show the other children. You can easily teach them how to make them.'

So the next day Peter and Jean took the fir cone girls to school and set them on the class table for the others to see.

'How lovely!' said Miss Brown, their teacher. 'I believe they would sell very well at our school Christmas Fair, Peter and Jean. They are most amusing, and cleverly done too. Could you make some more, do you think?'

Well, of course, they could – and they did too. And at the school Christmas Fair Peter and Jean had a table all to themselves, full of fir cone girls they had made. They did feel proud.

'Aren't we lucky to have a mother who can make things like this with us?' said Jean. 'We did have fun.'

I expect your mother would make some fir cone girls with you too, if you asked her. Wouldn't you like to make a fir cone family?

Heyho and the
North Wind

Heyho and the North Wind

ONCE UPON a time, Heyho the brownie was washing his clothes on a very windy day. He washed a pair of blue socks, six blue handkerchiefs, a red shirt and a yellow tunic. Then he took up his lovely new scarf and put that into the soapy water too.

Heyho was very proud of his scarf. It was yellow with an orange border, and was the nicest one in the whole of his village. The fairy queen herself had given it to him for a present when he had once stopped her runaway rabbits. They were pulling her carriage, and had been frightened at something – and off they went through the woods, helter-skelter, with the frightened fairy queen pulling hard at the reins.

Then Heyho had run out from the bushes and caught hold of the reins, stopping the rabbits at once. The queen was very grateful, and by the next post had come the lovely yellow scarf in return for the brownie's bravery.

So you can guess Heyho was proud of it, and he washed it very carefully indeed. Then he wrung it out and hung it up on the line to dry. Eight-Legs the spider had given him some of his strongest thread and it made a very nice washing line.

Heyho emptied his washtub and put the soap away. Then he went indoors to make himself a cup of cocoa, for he was rather thirsty after so much washing.

'It's a good thing it's such a windy day,' said Heyho to himself. 'It will dry the clothes quickly.'

'*Whoo-oo-oo!*' roared the wind outside. It was the North Wind, and it sounded excited. It flapped the clothes to and fro and they all danced up and down.

Heyho finished his cocoa and went outside to see if

his clothes were drying. He felt the socks – yes, nearly dry. He felt the handkerchiefs – yes, quite dry – and the tunic and shirt were hardly wet at all – and the scarf – but dear me, where was the scarf?

Heyho's heart almost stopped beating. He looked up and down the line but there was no scarf to be seen. It was gone! What a dreadful thing!

The pegs were still there. The North Wind must have torn the scarf away and taken it for himself!

He saw it and thought it would do nicely for him, I expect, thought Heyho. *Oh, my lovely, lovely scarf that the fairy queen gave me! I must get it back, I really must!*

He sat down on the grass and wondered how he could get it back. He scratched his chin hard, rubbed his nose and frowned deeply. Then he thought of an idea.

'I'll go to the North Wind's house and ask him what he has done with it!' he said, jumping to his feet. 'He has no right to steal my scarf like that! I'll make him give it back to me!'

So he locked up his little house, and took the key to Twiddle, his next-door neighbour.

'Where are you going all of a sudden?' asked Twiddle in surprise.

'To the house of the North Wind,' said Heyho fiercely. 'He has stolen my scarf, and I'm going to get it back!'

'Oh, Heyho, you are brave!' cried Twiddle. 'The North Wind is very big and very strong. I should be afraid to go and see him. People say that he has a dreadful temper too!'

'Well, I hope I come back all right,' said Heyho, feeling a bit shaky. 'Anyway, here's my key, Twiddle. Keep it for me, will you?'

So Twiddle said he would, and Heyho marched off northwards. He went up seven hills and down again. He crossed ten rivers, and went over twelve stiles. He walked through five woods, and then far away in the distance he saw the mountain on the top of which was the house of the North Wind.

It was very cold. Snowflakes floated about in the air and Heyho wished that he had his nice warm scarf tied tightly round his neck. He felt very cross indeed with the North Wind. He began to climb the mountain, and soon he was quite out of breath. He would never have got to the top if a large eagle had not kindly offered him a lift.

'My nest is nearly at the top,' said the eagle. 'I will take you as far as that, if you like.'

So Heyho gladly climbed on to the bird's soft back, and soon he was nearly at the top of the steep mountain. The eagle shook him off, and he said thank you and went on again up the winding path.

Soon he saw the house of the North Wind. It was a funny sort of house, for, although it had openings for windows and doors, it had no glass in the windows and no doors in the entrances. Heyho thought it must be a very cold house to live in.

At last he got to the front doorway. He could see no sign of the North Wind, but he heard a loud snoring noise. He peeped in at the front doorway and at first saw nothing. Then he made out a great bed, and lying on it was the North Wind, an enormous person, very billowy looking. He was fast asleep and snoring.

Oh dear! thought Heyho. *He won't be very pleased at being woken up.*

The brownie stood and looked at the North Wind for a few minutes, and then he made up his mind. He must wake him! So he stepped into the doorway and went up to the bed.

'Hey, North Wind!' he said. 'Wake up!'

The North wind didn't stir. So Heyho shouted more loudly still, 'Hey, North Wind! Wake up, I say!'

He poked the North Wind with his finger and made him stir. Then with an enormous yawn the wind sat up and rubbed his eyes. He looked so big that Heyho's knees began to shake and he could hardly stand up.

Then the North Wind suddenly saw Heyho and stared in surprise.

'What did you wake me for?' he asked crossly.

'I've come to ask you to give me back my yellow scarf,' Heyho said boldly. 'You took it this morning.'

'What? You've come to wake me up for a silly thing like that!' cried the North Wind angrily. 'I'll blow you to the other end of the world!'

He stooped down and was just going to blow the brownie right out of the house when Heyho caught hold of his nose and held on tight. That just saved him, for though he was lifted right off his feet by the force of the wind, he wasn't blown away.

'Ow! Oh!' cried the North Wind. 'Let go of my nose, you horrid little brownie!'

'Well, don't blow me away then!' said Heyho. 'And let me tell you this, North Wind – the fairy queen will be very angry when she hears that you have taken my scarf. She gave it to me herself!'

'Ooh!' said the North Wind. 'I didn't know that. The fairy queen, eh? Well, well! Why didn't you tell me that at first?'

'You didn't give me a chance,' said the brownie. 'You nearly blew me away to the end of the world!'

'Well, I'm very sorry about your scarf,' said the North Wind. 'As a matter of fact, I did take it! It looked so bright hanging there that I thought I'd like a game with it. So I pulled it off the line and blew it right away.'

'Oh dear!' said Heyho. 'Do you know where it is now?'

'Well, I left it hanging over Wizard Wimple's chimney,' said the North Wind. 'It looked very funny there, I can tell you.'

'My poor scarf!' groaned Heyho. 'Well, you'll have to take me to Wizard Wimple's to get it back, North Wind.'

'Easy!' cried the wind, and lifted Heyho up into the air in a trice. He blew him along at a terrific speed and put him down *bump*, just outside Wizard Wimple's cottage. Heyho looked up at the chimney – but alas! There was no yellow scarf there!

'That's funny!' said the North Wind. 'Let's ask what he's done with it.'

'You go!' said Heyho nervously. 'I'm not very fond of wizards.'

So the North Wind banged at the door and the wizard's black cat answered it.

'Where's the scarf that was hanging over the chimney?' demanded the North Wind.

'So it was you who put it there!' said the cat. 'Well, my master was very cross about it. He has given it to Witch Widdershins to make a spell with. She wanted a scarf just like that.'

'Oh dear!' cried Heyho in dismay. 'Quick, North Wind, take me to Witch Widdershins before she uses my lovely scarf for her horrid spells.'

The North Wind caught up Heyho once more and blew him off to Witch Widdershins' cottage in the middle of a thick wood. He knocked at the door and the witch looked out of the window.

'What do you want?' she asked crossly.

'The yellow scarf that the wizard gave you,' answered the wind. 'Have you used it for a spell yet?'

'No,' said the witch. 'It wasn't quite the right colour after all. So I gave it to Mr Biscuits, the man who sells me my bread. He lives at the other side of the wood.'

She banged the window down and the wind turned to poor Heyho.

'Well, we'd better go to Mr Biscuits,' he said. 'My, this is a journey, isn't it?'

Off they went again, and soon arrived at Mr Biscuits' shop. He was baking bread, and when he came out to see them he was covered with flour.

'Do you want to buy my loaves?' he asked.

'No,' said the wind. 'We want that yellow scarf that Witch Widdershins gave you. It belongs to Heyho.'

'Oh, I gave it to my little girl, Cherry Bun,' said Mr Biscuits. 'She has gone on an errand to Mother Buttercup up the hill.'

'We'll go and meet her,' said the wind. So once again Heyho was whisked off. He was put down just by a little girl – but she was not wearing the yellow scarf.

'Is your name Cherry Bun?' asked the North Wind. The little girl nodded. 'Well, where's that yellow scarf, little girl?'

'I've g-g-given it to my f-f-friend,' said Cherry Bun, rather frightened to see such an enormous person as the North Wind. 'The colour didn't suit me, and she gave me a little blue purse in exchange. Would you like that instead?'

She held out the purse, but Heyho shook his head.

'No, I want my scarf,' he said. 'Where does your friend live?'

'Over there in Higgledy village,' said Cherry Bun. So off went the wind and the brownie once more. They soon arrived at Higgledy and asked for Cherry Bun's friend. When they found her, they looked in vain for the scarf.

'Oh, an elf came by and saw me wearing it, and he said it didn't belong to me, so he took it away,' said the little girl, with tears in her eyes. 'I don't know where he went to.'

Heyho felt like crying too! It seemed as if he never would get his scarf back!

'I'm hungry and tired,' said the North Wind. 'Let's buy some buns and chocolate, Heyho, and have a picnic.'

So they did, and after that they felt better. Then they hunted all over the countryside for the elf, but couldn't find him.

'Well, I'm really very sorry,' said the North Wind. 'But I don't see that I can do any more for you, Heyho, except take you home. I'm very tired and I want to go back and finish my sleep.'

So he took Heyho home, and set him down on his own doorstep – and oh dear me, whatever do you think! Why, tied tightly round Heyho's shiny knocker was his lovely yellow scarf! Someone had put it there for him!

'Well!' cried the North Wind crossly. 'Here it is

after all! And you needn't have woken me up and made me rush around the country like that! I've a good mind to blow you to the end of—'

'Oh, no, you won't,' said Heyho. 'It was your fault to begin with, North Wind. You just go right back and finish your sleep, and don't be so cross!'

The North Wind puffed Heyho's hat off, and then flew away to his house on the mountain. Heyho picked up his hat, untied his scarf, and went to Twiddle's house to get his key.

'Oh!' said Twiddle when he opened the door. 'I'm so glad you're back, Heyho – and you needn't have bothered about your scarf after all! I happened to be walking out today and I saw a little girl wearing your lovely scarf. So I made her give it to me and brought it back for you – and I expect you found it tied round your door knocker, didn't you?'

'Yes, I did,' said Heyho. 'Thank you, Twiddle.'

He took his key, unlocked his little front door and made himself a cup of cocoa.

'Well!' he said. 'To think I've had all that flying about for nothing! I might just as well have stayed at home and read my new storybook!'

And so he might!

Scallywag's Mistake

Scallywag's Mistake

'LOOK! HERE'S Scallywag the imp, again,' said Mother Trot-Around. 'He's got a caravan now, and a little horse to pull it.'

'But he hasn't got any furniture,' said Mr Tiptap. 'He's trying to earn some money to get some, and he's come to our village to see if we'll give him any work.'

'Well, I won't,' said Dame Snappy. 'He's lazy and cheeky, and he never does a job properly. Why, when I told him to paint my shed for me, he did three sides and left the back unpainted, just because he thought I wouldn't notice it! But I did.'

'Yes, he's a lazy rascal,' said little Mrs Sharp-Eye.

'He won't get any work here – or in the next village either. My sister lives there and she told me that Scallywag went into her shed when she was out and took all her garden tools away! We'll be careful of that tiresome little imp!'

So when Scallywag left his caravan up in the woods and came down to the village to look for work, he found none.

'No thanks. We don't want you here,' said Mother Trot-Around, and shut her door with a bang.

'You go away!' said Mr Tiptap, and shook his stick at the cheeky Scallywag.

Dame Snappy and Mrs Sharp-Eye chased him away with their brooms and that made him very angry. He badly wanted to buy some furniture for his caravan, which was very uncomfortable to live in without carpets, chairs, bed or table.

I want a little oil stove too, thought Scallywag. *It's so very, very cold! Look at the white frost on the ground – and, goodness gracious me, the village pond is frozen over with thick ice. No wonder I'm cold at night in my empty caravan.*

It certainly was cold weather. Scallywag shivered as he went round the cottages asking for work. But nobody would give him any – nobody at all. He wasn't a nice person and nobody liked him one little bit.

Now, when it was getting dark, Scallywag came to a dear little cottage at the end of the village. He knocked. There was no answer. No light shone out of the windows, so Scallywag thought there must be nobody in. Then a voice from the house next door called to him.

'Hey! Little Miss Spindles has gone away for a few days. Who are you?'

Scallywag didn't answer. He crept round to the back. A sudden idea had come to him.

He peered in at the window. It was almost too dark to see inside, but he could just make out bits and pieces of furniture. Furniture! Just what he wanted and hadn't got. And Miss Spindles was away – so if her furniture went away too, nobody would know for some time! It would fit into his caravan nicely. He could take it away in his caravan and never come back to this village again!

But wait a minute – if he brought his caravan to the house from out of the wood, people would see it. They would guess that he, Scallywag, had taken the furniture. He mustn't fetch his caravan, that was plain.

He sat on the back step and thought hard. If he could take the furniture to some place bit by bit and hide it, then he could take his caravan there the next night and pick up all the chairs and things without anyone guessing what he was doing. But where could he hide the furniture?

An idea came to him and he grinned. 'Of course! I'll go to the pond. It's frozen over. I'll make a hole in it and poke in every bit of furniture. It will be well hidden under the ice. Nobody would possibly guess it was there. Then tomorrow I'll bring my caravan down to the pond-side and say that it's a more sheltered place there, and in the night I'll go to the hole I made and fish out the furniture bit by bit – and away I'll go before dawn with it safely in my caravan.'

This seemed a very good idea to Scallywag. It wasn't long before he had found a window he could open. In he went and ran to the front door. He opened it from the inside and peered out. Nobody about at all!

He brought out a little wooden chair and carried it to the pond. He made a hole in the ice and poked the chair into it. He tied a piece of string securely to it and left the string outside the hole. Then he went back to the cottage.

He brought out a little wooden table and poked that down into the hole too, pushing it under the ice. He tied a table leg to the string from the chair.

Then, when I come tomorrow night to collect everything, all I'll have to do is to pull the string, and the whole collection will come along to the hole, one bit of furniture after another, so that I can take each piece out! thought Scallywag. *How very, very clever I am!*

He brought another chair and a little sideboard to the hole. He had to make the hole a bit bigger for the sideboard, which was rather an awkward shape. Then back he went for another chair – and the grandfather clock too! It struck eight as he carried it, and he was frightened in case anyone heard it. But nobody was about.

He dragged Miss Spindles' dear little carved wooden bed along too, and that went down into the hole as well. He didn't bring the wardrobe because it really was too heavy. He pushed a stool, a small cupboard and a little chest of drawers under the ice, all linked together with the long piece of string. What an idea!

Then he went back and shut the door of the cottage. He crept up to the woods to his cold caravan and went inside gleefully. Aha! Tomorrow night he would have it full of lovely furniture and would be off and away before anyone knew about its loss!

But Miss Spindles happened to come home the

very next day, and when she opened her front door, what a shock she got! Where was her hall chair? Where was her little cupboard? And what in the world had happened to her parlour chairs and table? And dear me, where was her old grandfather clock – and her little bed? She gave a loud wail and rushed to tell her next-door neighbour. Soon the news was all over the village.

'Miss Spindles' furniture has gone! Someone broke in last night and took it. Find the thief!'

'I wouldn't be surprised if it's that horrid Scallywag,' said Dame Snappy. 'Let's go and look in his caravan.'

So they went – but, of course, there was no furniture there at all. Scallywag pretended to be angry.

'What! You come here and accuse me of taking furniture? I'll complain to the policeman! What a thing to say of an honest person like me! Wouldn't I have gone off in my caravan if I'd taken the furniture? And aren't I still here? Though, all the same, I'm moving today – down beside the pond because it's more sheltered there.'

'You'll just stay where you are till we've made a few more inquiries,' said Dame Snappy.

So Scallywag had to stay in his caravan up in the woods, while everyone went rushing around to try and find the lost furniture. Scallywag didn't mind. He could easily move down to the pond when it began to get dark.

But during that day the weather turned warm. The wind blew from the south instead of from the north. The frost disappeared. All the frozen puddles melted.

And the ice on the pond began to melt too! It cracked here and there. Puddles came on the thawing surface. The farmer's ducks came and tried the ice to see if they would soon be able to swim again.

At about three o'clock most of the ice had melted on the pond – and then the villagers saw strange things!

'Look! What are all those things bobbing about on the pond?' cried Mrs Sharp-Eye, pointing. 'There's something with four straight legs – and something else with a face.'

'It's a clock – and that four-legged thing is a wooden table, upside down!' said Mr Tiptap. 'Good gracious me – what a very peculiar thing!'

'And there's a chair, look!' said Mother Trot-Around. 'And is that a stool? Yes it is. My word – can all these things be Miss Spindles' lost furniture?'

The village policeman, Mr Plod, came and stared at all the bobbing bits and pieces. He looked at his notebook solemnly and nodded.

'Yes – I can see most of the furniture that is reported in my notebook – even the little cupboard. My goodness me – who has thrown it into the pond? How wicked!'

'Mr Plod,' said Dame Snappy, 'that furniture went last night, when the pond was frozen over. It must have been poked down through a hole in the ice, and left there – to be collected by someone! Aha – that someone didn't guess that the ice was going to melt!'

'Who's the someone?' asked Mr Plod.

'We'll know that all right, tonight,' said Dame Snappy. 'Though we can guess now, most of us! Mr Plod, let's all hide over there in those bushes and wait and see who comes to collect the furniture! He will come as soon as it is dark. No doubt about that!'

So away they went to the bushes and half the village hid itself there, waiting for the someone to come!

And presently there came the sound of wheels on the pond-side road, and in the darkness came Scallywag's caravan. He held a lantern over the pond to see if he could walk over the ice to the hole where he had hidden the furniture.

But there was no ice now – only a stretch of water, with lots of things bobbing up and down together on it!

'Good gracious! Who would have thought that the ice on the pond would melt so quickly?' groaned Scallywag. 'It's a mercy nobody saw all the furniture floating around. Now I shall have to wade out and fetch it – and the water's so very cold!'

He took his lantern and waded into the pond. Ooooh! How cold the water was! He waded in past his waist and at last came to a chair. He took hold of it. He began to walk back and everything bobbed along behind him in a row, because it was all tied together.

And when Scallywag had got everything out of the water, and had stood it on the bank, shivering as he did so, he heard a shout. He stopped untying the wet string and listened in fright.

'There he is, the thief! Catch him! He's got all the furniture! There he is!'

And out of the bushes tumbled the villagers, their lanterns lit, with Mr Plod in front. Scallywag ran to his caravan.

But it was too late. Scallywag was surrounded. Mr Plod took him by the shoulders. 'You must come along with me,' he said sternly. 'I want to know how you got all Miss Spindles' furniture.'

'It was in the p-p-pond,' stammered Scallywag desperately.

'Oh! You don't think anyone made a hole in the ice last night and hid it there, do you?' said Dame Snappy, shining her lantern on Scallywag's scared face.

'Dear me – that would be a d-d-dreadful thing to do,' said Scallywag.

'It certainly would. And what do you think should be done to a person who did a thing like that?' said Mr Tiptap fiercely.

Scallywag didn't know what to say, so he said nothing. Mrs Sharp-Eye tapped him smartly on the arm.

'A person who does a thing like that should most certainly be punished! He should spend the night in prison, he should polish all the furniture when it's dry again, and he should work in Miss Spindles' garden for four whole weeks to make up for his wrongdoings,' she said. 'Don't you think so, Scallywag?'

Scallywag nodded his head miserably. Oh dear, oh

dear – to think of the ice melting like that! How unlucky he was!

Well, Scallywag was punished. He was put into prison for three nights, not one. He had to polish up every bit of the stolen furniture when he came out – and it took him three weeks, because Miss Spindles was so very, very particular about it.

And after that he had to work four weeks in her garden for her and sleep locked up in her shed each night, in case he went off before his time was up.

'If I'd worked as hard as this before I'd have earned plenty of money to buy myself furniture for my caravan!' he groaned. 'Perhaps it's better to work and be honest after all!'

Then, just as he was leaving the village at last, a cold spell came again, and ice covered all the puddles. Scallywag stared at it as he went to get his caravan.

'Horrid ice! Stupid, annoying ice – it was all your fault I got into trouble. I'll stamp on you, I'll smash you to bits!'

He stamped on a frozen puddle. It was so slippery that he lost his balance. His feet slid from under him and he sat down with a bump. His horse took fright and galloped away with the caravan, leaving Scallywag sitting down on a frozen puddle, crying and wailing loudly.

Get up, Scallywag! Be sensible! Work hard and honestly and you'll be all right – and for goodness' sake, go after your horse and caravan before you lose them for ever!

The Proud Fir Tree

The Proud Fir Tree

THERE WAS once a beautiful fir tree that lived in a wood. It was the only fir tree there and it thought a good deal of itself.

The other trees around it were oak and beech and hazel, and they were none of them quite so tall as the fir.

Once some children had come into the wood and had seen the fir.

'Look!' said the boy. 'See that fir? Hasn't it got a lovely straight trunk? Did you know that the masts of ships are made from fir tree trunks, Rosie?'

'Are they really?' said Rosie, looking up the straight trunk of the fir.

'Yes – and telegraph poles too,' said the boy. 'Not many trees grow such fine straight trunks, Rosie.'

Well, the fir tree was tremendously proud to hear all this. It swayed about in the wind and made a little song up about itself:

'Telegraph poles are made from me,
And the masts of ships that sail on the sea!'

The other trees got tired of this song. 'After all, a good many things are made from us too,' said the oak. 'I make lots of beautiful furniture – and the beams in the roofs of many famous old buildings are made of oak.'

'And I am used for heaps of things too,' said the graceful beech.

'The gamekeeper comes and cuts his walking sticks from my branches,' said the hazel.

And even the little willow by the stream had something to say too. 'I help to make cricket bats,' it said.

When the autumn came, the beeches and the oaks and all the other trees in the wood flamed into brilliant colour. You should have seen them! The beech was a mass of gold.

The fir was quite jealous of them then. 'I suppose you think you are lovely, turning strange colours all of a sudden,' it said.

'Well, the children think we are lovely,' said the beech. 'They like to pick up some of my golden leaves and take them to school. And they pluck some of my sprays and press them so that they may have vases full of my golden leaves in the winter.'

'Let me tell you this,' said the fir. 'Every autumn you dress yourselves proudly in gold, red, brown and yellow. And then what happens to you? The frost comes along and loosens all your leaves – and the wind sweeps them off the boughs. Your fine dresses lie scattered on the muddy ground – and you are left bare and cold all through the winter days!'

'That is quite true,' said the oak.

'And what about me?' said the fir. 'It is true that I don't dress myself up in yellows and reds – but I am sensible enough to keep my branches green all the winter long! I don't stand cold and bare and ugly.'

The other trees knew that this was true. They waved their bare boughs in the wind, while the fir waved her green-clad branches in pride.

'Are we really ugly now?' said the oak sadly. 'I wonder why we shed our pretty leaves? It does seem rather a waste to have to grow them every year.'

'Perhaps the fir is more sensible than we are, after all,' said the hazel.

'Telegraph poles are made from me,
And the masts of ships that sail on the sea!'

sang the fir tree.

Now, that winter the sky suddenly became a strange grey leaden colour. The trees looked up, half afraid.

'Why is the sky so low and grey?' said the oak.

'I don't like it. And listen – the wind is getting up!'

A cold wind blew. The bare trees waved their branches and the fir tree shouted in the wind.

Then snow fell. It fell steadily all the night long. It didn't stop once. The sky was full of snow. When the morning came, the wood looked so different. It was quite white!

'What a snowstorm!' said the oak, shaking its sturdy boughs. The snow fell off at once.

But the oak's branches were soon white with snow again, for there was still plenty of snow to come. All day long it fell, and on the hills it was more than three feet deep.

Then the fir tree began to grumble loudly. 'Oh, this snow! Oh, this heavy, heavy snow! I can't bear the weight of it any longer!'

'Well, shake it off then, as we do,' said the oak.

'How can I?' said the fir tree crossly. 'You have bare branches, so that the snow cannot cling to you as it can to my green branches! I hold the snow with all my boughs. Oh, how heavy it is! Stop snowing, sky! I can bear the weight no longer!'

But the snow went on snowing. Then there came a loud CRACK! All the trees were startled. What could it be? They could see nothing.

'I'm afraid I am breaking,' said the fir tree sadly. 'That was one of my branches.'

CRACK! Another branch broke. The fir tree shivered. A mass of snow slipped down from its branches.

CRACK!

'Good gracious! The fir tree will be broken to bits!' said the oak. 'I do hope the snow soon stops.'

It stopped very soon. Then the weather turned warmer and all the snow melted. The trees stretched themselves and looked at the fir tree.

Poor, poor thing! All its beautiful branches were broken and hung sadly down. One was already on the ground. It was no longer beautiful.

'Why did I boast that I kept my leaves?' said the fir tree sadly. 'If I had thrown them down as you did, oak tree, the snow would have slipped easily from my boughs, and they would not have broken beneath the great weight of the snow. Oh, what an unhappy tree I am! I am ashamed of my looks now. I shall never, never sing my little song again.'

'We will grow our branches more closely around you to hide your broken sides,' promised the beech. 'After all, you still have a fine straight trunk.'

So the other trees grew their branches quite close to the fir, and hid the places where his dead branches had fallen off. He was grateful and friendly.

'Well, fir tree, you may not be so beautiful now, but you are much nicer to know!' said the oak next summer, when his leaves whispered by the thousand.

'That's something!' said the fir tree, stretching his high head to the sky. 'That's certainly something.'

The Winter
Wide-Awakes

The Winter
Wide-Awakes

MOTHER PUT her head in at the nursery door and saw a very cosy scene. There was a big fire burning, and three children were sitting by it. Two were playing a game of snap and the other was reading.

'Do you know who's here?' she said. 'Auntie Lou.'

'Oh!' said all three children, raising their heads. They were Tessie, Pat and Johnny. Tessie looked a little doubtful.

'I hope she hasn't come to take us for a walk,' she said. 'Auntie Lou is lovely to go for walks with in the summer, but it's all snowy outside now and very cold. I don't think I want to go out today.'

Another head came round the door. It belonged to Auntie Lou. She was dressed in warm tweeds and had a bright red scarf round her neck. Her head was bare, and her cheeks were as red as her scarf. Her blue eyes twinkled.

'What's this I hear? You don't want to go out with me? Well, I like that! Who came and begged to go out with me every week in the summer? Who went to find conkers and nuts and blackberries with me in the autumn because I knew all the best places?'

'We did,' said Pat with a grin. 'But Auntie Lou, we're so warm and cosy here, and there's nothing to see in the country now. Honestly there isn't.'

'There's nothing but snow,' said Johnny, 'and all the birds are gone and all the animals are asleep.'

'What a poor little ignorant boy!' said Auntie Lou, making a funny face. 'It's true we shouldn't see anything of the winter sleepers – they're all tucked away in their holes – but we could see plenty of wide-awakes.'

'Who are they?' asked Johnny.

'Well, as I came over the fields this morning to pay a call on three lazy children, I saw a beautiful red fox,' said Auntie Lou. 'He wasn't asleep. He almost bumped into me coming round the hedge. I didn't hear him and I suppose he didn't hear me.'

'Oh, a fox!' said Pat. 'I'd like to have seen that. Auntie, I'll come with you if you'll show me all the wide-awakes.'

'We'll all come,' said Tessie, shutting her book. 'I'd like to find some wide-awakes too, and some birds as well. Lots have gone away, but we've still plenty left, haven't we, Auntie?'

'Plenty,' said her aunt. 'Hurry up then. I'll give you three minutes to put on boots and coats.'

They were all ready quickly, for they knew perfectly well that Auntie Lou wouldn't wait for anyone who wasn't. They set off down the snowy garden path.

'You can see how many birds have been in your

garden this morning,' said Auntie Lou, pointing to some bird tracks in the snow. 'Look, that's where the sparrows have been. See the little footmarks all set out in pairs? That's because they hop with their feet together. And there are the marks of a running bird – his footmarks are behind one another.'

Johnny hopped with his feet together and then ran. He saw that he had left his first footmarks in pairs, but the other marks were spread out behind one another. Auntie Lou laughed. 'The footmarks of the Johnny-Bird,' she said.

By the frozen pond they came to other bird prints, and Tessie pointed to them. 'Ducks,' she said. 'You can see the marks of the webbing between their toes.'

'Yes. The poor things thought they might have a swim on the pond and came waddling up from the farm to see,' said Auntie Lou. 'I wonder what they think when they find they can't splash in the ice.'

They left the pond behind and struck across the fields. How lovely they were, all blanketed in snow! The hedges were sprinkled with snow too, but here and there the red hips showed the green, unripe ivy berries.

'Look, Auntie,' said Pat, pointing to some bark in the hedgerow which had been gnawed white. 'Who's been doing that? Somebody must have been very hungry to eat bark.'

'One of the most wide-awakes,' said Auntie Lou. She pointed to some tracks. 'Look, rabbit footmarks. The bunnies have been gnawing bark because they are so hungry.'

'But why don't they eat the grass?' said Tessie. The two boys laughed at her.

'How can they when it's deep down under the snow?' said Pat scornfully. 'Use your brains, Tessie!'

'Oh, I never thought of that,' said Tessie. 'Poor little rabbits – they must get awfully hungry when their grass is hidden away. No wonder they come and gnaw at the bark.'

'Yes, and the fox knows they will come out to feed

somewhere,' said Auntie Lou. 'So he comes out too, and pads along quietly in the snow, watching for an unwary rabbit. I saw a sad little scattering of grey fur this morning as I came along, to show me where the fox had made his breakfast.'

'Look, what's that?' suddenly whispered Johnny, clutching at his aunt's arm. She looked where he was pointing.

'A stoat,' she said. 'He's after the rabbits, I expect.'

'But he's white,' said Johnny, amazed. 'He wasn't white when we saw him in the summer.'

'Ah, he's clever. He changed his dark coat for a white one in the winter when the snow came –' said his aunt – 'all but the tip of his tail, which is black. Now his enemies can't see him against the white snow.'

'Isn't he clever?' said Pat. 'He's cleverer than the fox. *He* doesn't change his red coat to white. Does the stoat always change his coat, Auntie Lou?'

'Only in cold climates,' said his aunt, 'not down in the south where it is warmer and there is little snow in the winter. Now look, what's that?'

'A weasel,' said Pat. 'He's wide awake too, isn't he? Look at him, going along almost like a slinky snake. He's a fierce, lively little fellow.'

They went by another farm. The farmer was standing at the door of his cowshed and hailed them.

'Good morning. It's a fine morning for a walk, isn't it? It's a pity I can't send my cows out for a walk too. They're tired of standing in their sheds.'

'Farmer Toms, have you lots of mice and rats about?' asked Johnny. 'We're out looking for wide-awake creatures today, and we've seen plenty; but we've seen no rats nor mice.'

'Ah, I've too many – far too many,' said the farmer. 'Up in the loft there, where I store my grain, I get no end of the creatures. You go up and maybe you'll see some.'

They all climbed the ladder and went into the dark loft. They sat down on sacks and kept quiet. Almost at once they heard a squeaking. Then two mice appeared from a hole and scampered over to a bin.

'There are two,' called Tessie, but her voice frightened them of course, and they turned to run away; then a rat suddenly appeared and made a dart at one of the mice. Tessie gave a squeal.

'Oh! A rat! Horrid, sharp-nosed thing! Auntie, I don't like rats. Let's go down.'

The mice disappeared and the rat slunk away too. He was a thin rat and looked very hungry. Perhaps he wasn't very clever at catching mice. Nobody liked the look of him.

'The rat is every animal's enemy and ours as well,' said Auntie Lou. 'I haven't anything good to say of him. We should get rid of him in every way we can.'

The mice squealed behind the boards. 'They are saying "Hear, hear!"' said Pat, and that made everyone laugh.

They went down the ladder and told Farmer Toms what they had seen. Then they went into the shed. The cows smelt nice and turned their big heads to look at the children.

'Where are your sheep?' asked Johnny.

The farmer waved his hand up to the hills. 'Away up there in the snow with the shepherd,' he said. 'He's got them safe and is expecting their little lambs soon. They're often born in the snowy weather and they're none the worse for it. You must go and see them when they are born.'

The children left the farm and went on their way.

'I wouldn't have believed there was so much to see on a snowy, wintry day,' said Tessie. 'I really wouldn't. Why, it's as interesting as summertime.'

'Look, there's a thrush – and a blackbird too – eating the hips in the snowy hedge,' said Pat. 'Aren't they enjoying themselves? What a good thing there are berries to feed the hungry birds in the winter!'

'And look at all those chaffinches,' said Tessie, as a flock of the bright little birds flew over her head towards the farm. 'I've never seen so many chaffinches together before.'

'No, in the spring and summer they go about in pairs,' said her aunt. 'But many birds in winter like to flock together. They are probably going to see if there is any grain round about the farm for them to peck up. Look up into the sky – you'll see some other birds there that flock by the thousand.'

'Peewits!' said Johnny. 'Don't their wings twinkle as they fly? I do love their call too – just like their name!'

'I should think we've seen all the winter wide-awakes there are now,' said Tessie. But Auntie Lou shook her head.

'No, there's another. I saw him this morning as I came through the hazel wood. He *has* been asleep, but this lovely sunny day woke him up. He doesn't mind the snow a bit. Look, there he is, the pretty thing!'

A squirrel suddenly bounded down a tree trunk and ran right over to the children. Auntie Lou put her hand in her pocket and took out a few shelled nuts. 'Here you are,' she said to the amusing little squirrel. 'I've shelled them for you, so you won't have any bother today.'

The squirrel took a nut from her fingers, skipped away a few paces, then sat up with the nut in his paws and began to eat it quickly. The children watched him in delight.

'He's a great friend of mine,' said Auntie Lou. 'If he's awake and I walk through this wood, he always comes along to me to see if I've anything for him. I expect he has plenty of nuts and acorns hidden away, but he does love a peanut or brazil nut all ready shelled for him – it makes a change from his own nuts.'

'Let's take him home! Oh, do let's take him home!' said Johnny, and he tried to catch the bushy-tailed squirrel, but in a trice the little creature ran up a nearby trunk, his tail out behind him, and sat high above their heads, making a little chattering noise.

'His home is up in that tree,' said Auntie Lou. 'I've no doubt he has a very cosy hole there, safe from little boys who want to take him home with them.'

'Oh, I do like him,' said Johnny. 'Perhaps in the

spring, when he has tiny young squirrel children I could have one of those. I'd love a squirrel pet. I'd call him Scamper.'

The squirrel disappeared into his home. Auntie Lou began to walk through the trees. 'It's time we went home too,' she said. 'Look how the sun is sinking. It will soon be getting dark. Come along.'

They ran after her, looking about for more squirrels, but they saw none. Johnny made up his mind to go to the woods the very next day and make friends with the little squirrel all by himself.

'He's the nicest winter wide-awake we've seen,' he said. 'What a lot we've met today, Auntie! I'd no idea there were so many birds and animals to see on such a wintry day.'

It began to get dark. 'We shan't see any more now,' said Tessie. But they did! As they walked down the lane home, a little bird kept pace with them, flying from tree to tree as they went, giving them little bursts of song.

'It's a robin,' said Auntie Lou. 'He is always the latest bird abed. Maybe he's the one that belongs to your garden, children. Look out for him tomorrow, and scatter some crumbs for him.'

'We will,' said Tessie, opening the garden gate. The robin flew in before her. 'Yes, he must be ours. He has come to welcome us home. Auntie, you're coming in to tea, aren't you?'

'Of course,' said Auntie Lou. 'I think I deserve a very nice tea, with hot scones and homemade jam, after taking you three children out to see so many wide-awakes.'

'You do! You do!' chorused the children.

And she did, didn't she? I hope you'll see a lot of wide-awakes if *you* go out on a winter's day.

Mr Twiddle and the Snowman

Mr Twiddle and
the Snowman

ONE DAY the children who lived next door to Mr Twiddle made a fine snowman in his garden. Mrs Twiddle said they might, because the Twiddle's garden was so much bigger than theirs. So the children were very pleased, and they built a big man, quite as tall as their daddy, and very fat and round.

'Mrs Twiddle, Mrs Twiddle, can we have an old hat for his head and an old scarf for his neck?' called the children, looking in at the kitchen window, where Mrs Twiddle was making cakes.

'Yes,' said Mrs Twiddle. 'You'll find an old hat in the hall and a ragged old scarf somewhere by it. And if you look in the hall drawer you'll maybe find an old pair of gloves too, for the snowman's cold hands!'

'Oh, good!' shouted the children, and they tore off to get the clothes. They found them all – and they found Mr Twiddle's stick too, which they borrowed for their funny old snowman.

My word, he did look grand when he was finished and dressed up! You should have seen him, with Mr Twiddle's old hat on his head, a scarf tied loosely round his fat neck, raggedy gloves on his round hands, and a stick through his arm! Really, he looked very fine indeed, and the children were proud of him.

Mrs Twiddle looked out of the window and laughed. 'He just wants a pipe to stick in his mouth,' she said, 'then he'll be happy. Here is one of Mr Twiddle's.'

So the children stuck a pipe in the snowman's mouth and then danced round him, laughing. Their mother rang the tea bell next door and they hurried off, hungry and happy, wondering what Mr Twiddle would say when he saw their wonderful snowman.

Well, Mr Twiddle didn't come home till it was almost dark, for he had been to see his brother in the next village. He stumped in at the front gate, tired and hungry – and then he suddenly saw the old snowman standing quite still in his front garden.

'Hallo!' said Mr Twiddle in surprise. 'Who's that? What are you doing here, my good man?'

The good man didn't answer. Mr Twiddle grew cross.

'You needn't think I can't see you, standing there, trying to hide from me in the darkness!' he said. 'You are up to no good, I'll be bound! What are you waiting there for?'

The snowman said nothing at all. Mr Twiddle marched right up to him and looked at him as closely as he could in the half-darkness. And he saw that the snowman had got *his* hat on!

'You've got my hat!' he said in a rage. 'My dear old

comfortable hat! How dare you take my hat! Give it to me at once!'

The snowman didn't give it to Mr Twiddle. He just stood quite still and stared at him out of his big stone eyes.

'And you've got my scarf on, I do declare!' roared Mr Twiddle. 'Yes, you have! What next, I'd like to know! I suppose you've been sneaking around my house, just taking whatever you can put your hands on! I'll fetch a policeman! I'll give you such a smack that you'll land in the next-door garden!'

The snowman stared and said nothing. 'Can't you answer me?' shouted Mr Twiddle. 'Haven't you got a tongue in your head?'

The poor old snowman hadn't got a tongue of any sort, so he couldn't say a word. He just stood there in Mr Twiddle's hat and scarf, looking very large and miserable.

'And if you haven't got my gloves and my stick!' cried Mr Twiddle, suddenly seeing them in the darkness, and feeling them. 'This is too much! My hat, my scarf – and now my gloves and my stick! You are a wicked robber, and if you don't give me back my things at once, this very minute, I'll go out and get a policeman! Now!'

The snowman didn't move. Then a bit of snow melted by his mouth and his pipe fell out. Mr Twiddle picked it up.

'And you've got my pipe too!' he shouted. 'My very nicest, oldest pipe! What next! Are you wearing my vests and my socks and my best shirt under that large white overcoat of yours? Oh, you bad, wicked robber!'

Just then the village policeman came by and heard the shouting. He walked into the front garden.

'Now then, what's all this?' he asked.

'Oh, policeman, I'm glad you've come,' said Mr Twiddle. 'This robber won't give me back my clothes that he's stolen. He must be deaf and dumb, for he won't even say a word to me.'

Mr Twiddle suddenly slipped on the snow and fell

against the snowman. He clutched at him and one of the snowman's stone buttons fell off and hit Mr Twiddle sharply on the nose.

'Oh, you wicked fellow, you hit me!' shouted Mr Twiddle in a rage. 'Take that – and that – and that!'

He slapped the snowman hard and the snow fell off in big pieces. Mr Twiddle was astonished. He hit the snowman again and the funny old snowman began to fall to bits. Mr Twiddle fell on top of him and floundered about in the snow, shouting and smacking. The policeman pulled him up, just as Mrs Twiddle came to the door in astonishment, holding a lantern to see what was the matter.

'Twiddle! What are you doing?' she called. 'Are you being rude to the policeman?'

'No, madam he isn't,' said the policeman, with a grin. 'He's fighting a big snowman and breaking him all to bits!'

'Really, Mr Twiddle!' said Mrs Twiddle, in surprise. '*Must* you do a thing like that? And look at the mess you're in! Good gracious me – and you've spoilt your new hat and broken your nice new stick! Well, you'll have to use your old ones again. The snowman has got them, so you can bring them in with you before he melts all over them.'

Poor Mr Twiddle! He couldn't think of a word to say – not a word! He went into the kitchen, all covered with snow, and Mrs Twiddle shooed him out again.

'I'm not going to let you cover my nice kitchen floor with melting snow!' she cried. 'Shake yourself in the yard, please! And chop up your broken stick – it will do for firewood!'

Mr Twiddle went to the woodshed very gloomily. He took the chopper – and, oh dear me, he chopped up his hat and then went to hang his broken stick on the peg! There really is no knowing what he'll do next!

What a Good
Thing!

'What a Good Thing!

'YOU CAN all go out for a walk this morning,' said Mother to Jean, Harry and Peter. 'It's a lovely day.'

'Oh, good!' said Jean. 'Can we go down to the river, Mother? There may be a few boats out.'

'Very well,' said Mother. 'But just you be very careful so as not to fall in!'

'It's so nice and sunny,' said Peter. 'I guess we'll be as hot as can be! Need we put our coats on, Mother?'

'Of course you must!' said Mother. 'It isn't summer now. And scarves, please! There's a cold north wind blowing, and I certainly don't want you all in bed with colds.'

'Oh, Mother! Scarves too! We shall be cooked,' said Harry.

'Well, you must be cooked then,' said Mother firmly. 'Coats and scarves, please, and no nonsense.'

The children were cross about the scarves. They all hated scarves and gloves and wellington boots, and simply would not put them on if they could get out of it.

They went to the cloakroom and took down their coats. Just then the doorbell rang and Jean peeped into the hall to see who it was.

'It's Mrs Jones,' she said to the others. 'She'll keep Mother talking all morning. We'd better not go and say goodbye, or she'll keep us talking too.'

'We can all slip out of the back way then,' said Harry. 'Come on, everyone!'

'I say – as Mother won't see us go, shall we forget to put our scarves on?' said naughty Peter. 'It's so hot.'

'It is hot,' said Harry. 'We really shall be cooked in them. But Mother did say we were to put them on.'

'But she won't know if we don't,' said Peter.

'Peter, don't be so perfectly horrid!' said Jean. 'You know Mother trusts us to do what she says. I call that downright deceitful. It's just simply dreadful of you! Anyone would think you didn't love Mother when you talk like that.'

'Well, I do,' said Peter sulkily.

'You'd better show it then,' said Jean, tying her long woollen scarf firmly round her neck. Harry tied his scarf on too, looking rather red. Peter stood sulkily in the cloakroom. The others didn't wait for him. They ran out into the garden and made their way to the gate that led into the lane.

After a minute Peter joined them. Harry and Jean looked at his neck. He had tied his scarf round just as they had. Jean was glad. It made her angry and unhappy when Peter was deceitful. She took his arm.

'Good old Peter!' she said. But Peter was still rather sulky and he shook off Jean's arm. So she let him walk by himself and ran on ahead with Harry.

They soon came to the river. There had been a lot of rain and the river was swollen and ran very fast. The children threw bits of stick into it and watched them whirl away.

Soon they met George and Mary, and began to play games with them. George had a ball, and the children stood in a ring and threw the ball to one another. If somebody missed, they had to kneel on one knee. If they missed again, they had to kneel on both knees. It was such great fun!

Suddenly the ball went crooked and Mary couldn't catch it. It rolled away and away – right to the edge of the river. Mary raced after it, afraid it would roll right into the river.

But it didn't. It stopped just at the edge. Mary stooped to pick it up and caught her foot on a root. She fell – rolled down the bank – and splash! There she was in the river.

George gave a scream.

'Mary can't swim! Mary can't swim! Quick, oh do

come and save her!'

The four frightened children raced to the river and looked down into the water. Mary had been swept out a little way, and had caught hold of an old branch that had fallen into the bed of the river and stuck there. It just saved her from being swept right away with the current.

'Save me, save me!' cried Mary. 'This branch won't last very long. It's cracking already!'

'If only we had a rope!' cried Harry in despair. 'How can we save Mary? There's no one about. Oh, what shall we do? What shall we do?'

The branch that Mary was clinging to gave a loud crack. Mary screamed.

'Quick! Quick! The river is taking me away. The branch is breaking!'

'Jean! Harry! Take off your scarves and give them to me!' cried Peter suddenly, tearing his own scarf off his neck. 'Quick! I'm going to knot them together – and then I think they will just reach Mary.'

The three children tore off their long woollen scarves. Peter knotted them all together quickly and tightly. Then, with the other children holding on tightly to his waist so that he should not fall in, he bent over the bank and swung the scarf-rope right out over the river to poor Mary.

Crack! The branch broke in two. The little girl was swept away – but she just managed to snatch at the scarf-rope. She held on as tightly as she could – and Peter held on too.

'Hold tight, hold tight!' he yelled. 'I'll pull you in. But do hold tight. The scarves are very strong.'

With the others holding him fast, the little boy pulled hard at the scarf-rope. Slowly Mary came nearer the bank. At last she reached it. Peter lay flat and reached his hands to her. She was pulled up to the grass above, dripping wet, frightened and cold – but safe!

'Oh, thank you, Peter!' sobbed Mary.

Even George was crying, for he had been very frightened. 'You are so clever! However did you think of making a rope with those scarves? Oh, Peter – just suppose you hadn't worn your scarves today!'

'We almost didn't,' said Peter in a small voice. 'I think I was rather mean about it – but I'm jolly glad I did just what Mother said now!'

'So are we!' cried Harry and Jean, and they both gave Peter a big hug. 'Come on, Mary – you must get home straight away and be dried.'

So off they all went – and, you know, they never forgot that they saved Mary's life by obeying their mother that morning. You simply never know, do you!

Brer Rabbit Lays
in His Winter
Stores

Brer Rabbit Lays in His Winter Stores

NOW ONE time the winter set in very early and the creatures couldn't seem to find enough to eat. Brer Fox got as thin as a broom handle, and Brer Rabbit was just a bag of bones.

One day they met in the road and began to talk.

'Bad times, Brer Rabbit, bad times,' said Brer Fox.

'You've nothing to grumble at, Brer Fox,' said Brer Rabbit. 'You've got a horse and cart and I've got nothing except my old wheelbarrow!'

'What's the use of a horse and cart?' said Brer Fox. 'You just tell me that, Brer Rabbit – what's the use of a horse and cart when you've got nothing to carry in it?

Why, I used to go to the town and bring back my cart full of food – but now the horse is lazing in the field and the cart is lying idle in the shed.'

'That's bad,' said Brer Rabbit. 'Why don't you sell your horse and cart, Brer Fox, and buy food with the money? I'm surprised that a clever man like you hasn't thought of that before.'

Well, Brer Fox thought it over and he reckoned it was a mighty good idea. Having a horse and cart wouldn't help him if he was dying of hunger!

'Well,' said Brer Fox, 'that's a good idea, Brer Rabbit – but if I go to town and sell my horse and cart to buy food, I'll have no cart to bring it home in and no horse to pull it! So I'd be no better off than before!'

'Well, Brer Fox,' said Brer Rabbit, 'I don't mind giving you a hand over this. I'll lend you my wheelbarrow to bring your shopping home in. We can put the wheelbarrow in the cart when we set out, and after you've sold your horse and cart, you can buy food with the money and put it into my barrow. We can take turns in wheeling it home!'

'That's mighty good of you, Brer Rabbit,' said Brer Fox. 'I'll do that. Meet me at the corner of the road tomorrow morning and we'll set off for town.'

So the next morning the two of them set off in the cart. Brer Fox clucked to his horse and they galloped into the town. Pretty soon Brer Fox had sold the horse and cart and had money to jingle in his pockets.

My, the food he bought! It just made old Brer Rabbit's mouth water, so it did! A sack of rice, a sack of corn, a sack of coffee, a sack of turnips – it was a wonder it all went into the barrow!

'You take a turn at wheeling the barrow first, Brer Rabbit,' said Brer Fox. 'My arms ache from driving the horse.'

Brer Rabbit lifted the handles of the barrow. My, but it was heavy! Brer Rabbit puffed and panted and Brer Fox grinned to see him. Brer Fox walked fast and Brer Rabbit couldn't keep up with him. He did his best, but Brer Fox always seemed to manage to keep so far ahead that Brer Rabbit couldn't shout loudly enough to him to make him hear.

Well, at last Brer Rabbit's arms were aching so much that he had to put the barrow down.

'Heyo, Brer Fox!' he yelled. 'You come along back here! It's your turn now!'

Brer Fox went skipping along in front and didn't so much as turn his head.

'Brer Fox! BRER FOX! You come along back here!' yelled Brer Rabbit. 'I'm not going to wheel your food all the way home. You give me my share for helping you and I'll take it and go.'

Brer Fox heard that all right. He turned round and grinned at Brer Rabbit.

'The food's mine!' he shouted. 'I may give you a handful of rice, Brer Rabbit, but that's all you'll get! Aha! Someone else can play tricks, as well as you!'

Brer Rabbit thought mighty hard, he did. Then he shouted to Brer Fox.

'All right, Brer Fox. Just give me my handful of

rice and I'll be off. But you might pop into Brer Bear's house just over there and ask him for a little bag to put my rice in. I can't carry it in my paws very well!'

So Brer Fox, grinning to himself and feeling mighty pleased with things, popped along to Brer Bear's house and borrowed the smallest bag he could.

Now as soon as Brer Fox was out of sight, Brer Rabbit took hold of the sack of rice and pulled it out of the barrow. He hid it under a bush, but before he left it there he put his hand in at the top and got a handful of rice grains out. He ran back to the barrow and then set off in the opposite direction, dropping the rice as he went. Then back he went to the barrow again and sat down by it, pretending to cry.

By and by Brer Fox came back with a small bag, and when he got there he saw Brer Rabbit crying. My, but he was boo-hooing!

'In the name of goodness, Brer Rabbit, what's the matter?' said Brer Fox.

'Matter enough, matter enough!' said Brer Rabbit.

'I wish you'd stayed here instead of going off, Brer Fox.'

'What's up then, Brer Rabbit?'

'Oh, a man came, Brer Fox, and stole your lovely bag of rice!' sobbed Brer Rabbit. 'I ran after him but he went too fast for me.'

'Which way did he go, Brer Rabbit?'

'There's the way he went, Brer Fox, there's where he dropped the rice out of the sack as he ran. If you're quick, Brer Fox, you'll catch him!'

Brer Fox dropped the bag he carried and tore off, hoping to catch the man that Brer Rabbit spoke of. He was hardly out of sight when Brer Rabbit caught hold of the bag of coffee and carried that away to the bush and hid it too. He put his hand into the top of the sack, took out some coffee beans, ran back to the barrow, and then set off in the other direction, dropping the beans as he went. It looked just as if someone had run there with a sack, dropping beans out of it as he ran!

After a while, back came Brer Fox, a-puffing and

a-panting. He hadn't seen any man at all. Brer Rabbit shouted to him.

'You haven't come a minute too soon, Brer Fox! While you were gone another man came and carried off the coffee. See, that's the way he went, Brer Fox, and if you're quick, you'll catch him!'

Well, Brer Fox set off again as fast as he could, and he ran and ran, but he didn't see any man at all. While he was gone Brer Rabbit carried off the sack of corn, and sprinkled some grains in the opposite direction again. Then Brer Fox came back, shouting that he hadn't seen anyone – and Brer Rabbit yelled to him to say that another man had been and had carried off the corn.

Well, this suddenly seemed mighty strange to Brer Fox – all these man coming by that way, in a lonely place, and stealing out of his barrow. He wondered if maybe Brer Rabbit was up to one of his tricks, so when he ran off, pretending to chase the man again, he didn't go very far, but turned round and crept back to see what Brer Rabbit was doing.

And he was just in time to see Brer Rabbit pulling at the sack of turnips in his barrow! Well, Brer Fox was mighty tired with running hither and thither and backwards and forwards, but he felt so mad when he saw what Brer Rabbit was up to that he dashed up to him and shouted at him.

'What are you going to do with that sack of turnips?' he yelled.

Brer Rabbit put the sack down and looked very upset. He looked at Brer Fox as if he felt mighty sorry for folks who asked such foolish questions. He shook his head, he did, and said, 'Well, well, well! Who'd have thought Brer Fox would have come yelling at me like this, when anyone would guess I was just a-carrying it off to save for him, so's no man could steal it?'

But this sort of talk didn't deceive Brer Fox, and he snarled so fiercely that Brer Rabbit thought it would be better to run – and run he did, with Brer Fox at his tail, between the trees. And at last Brer Rabbit came to a hollow tree and in he went!

Well, old Brer Buzzard was a-sailing round in the air, and Brer Fox called to him.

'Just you watch this hole for me, Brer Buzzard,' said Brer Fox. 'I'm a-going to fetch some fire to smoke old Brer Rabbit out!'

Well, Brer Fox set off, and Brer Buzzard settled down beside the hole – and after a bit Brer Rabbit sang out, 'I've got the better of you, Brer Buzzard! I surely have!'

'How's that, Brer Rabbit?' said Brer Buzzard.

'Because I can see you and you can't see me!' said Brer Rabbit, in his most cheeky voice.

With that Brer Buzzard stuck his head in the hole of the tree and looked up to see Brer Rabbit, and no sooner did he do this than Brer Rabbit flung a handful of sand down into his eyes.

Poor Brer Buzzard! He blinked and he winked but he couldn't get the sand out – so down to the stream he flew to wash his eyes. And while he was gone, Brer Rabbit came down out of the hollow tree and raced back to the barrow.

It wasn't long before he had taken the sacks of corn, rice and coffee out from under the bush where he had hidden them, popped them into the barrow with the sack of turnips, and trundled away merrily to his home.

And my, didn't Brer Fox shake his fist when he passed by Brer Rabbit's house the next day and smelt fried rice cakes and fresh coffee! Ah, it's no use trying to trick Brer Rabbit!

Mr Meddle and
the Snow

Mr Meddle and the Snow

ONE MORNING when Mr Meddle got up he saw that it was snowing. Dear me, how it snowed! It snowed all night and it snowed all day.

'Just like great big goose feathers coming down from the sky,' said Mr Meddle, as he watched the snowflakes falling.

He rattled the pennies in his pocket. Mr Meddle had four of them there – and that was all the money he had. It wouldn't buy very much. Somehow or other he must get some more.

'I think I'll go and see if anyone wants their snow sweeping away,' said Mr Meddle. 'If I take my broom and my spade I might be able to earn quite a lot of money.'

So he found his broom and his spade and put them over his shoulder. Then off he went to find some work.

He came to Dame Fanny's cottage. She was at the window, looking up at the snow. Meddle called to her. 'Shall I sweep a path to your front door for you, Dame Fanny?'

'No, thank you!' called back Dame Fanny. 'I don't trust you to do anything sensibly, Mr Meddle!'

Meddle was angry. Of course he could act sensibly! How rude of Dame Fanny! He would sweep a path just to show her how well he could work. So, as soon as the old dame had gone from the window, Mr Meddle set to work.

He couldn't seem to find the proper path, so he swept hard where he thought it was. After he had swept quite a long time Dame Fanny looked out of the window again – and, my goodness, how angry she was!

'You're sweeping across my beds!' she shouted.

'All my snowdrops were coming up there – and now you have swept all their heads off! Look at them there in the snow, you mischievous creature! Just wait till I come out to you!'

But Meddle didn't wait! He shot off down the road as fast as his feet would take him. 'How was I to know she was growing silly snowdrops all over the place!' he grumbled. 'Oh, I say! Look at that great pile of snow by the side of the road there! How dreadful! I will dig it away and sweep it flat.'

So he began. He dug his spade into the big heap of snow and threw it behind him. Then he swept it over the pavement, feeling very pleased to think that he had got rid of such a big heap of snow.

But he had hardly finished when Mr Biscuit the baker, outside whose shop the big heap of snow had stood, suddenly put his head out of his door.

'And what do you think *you* are doing?' he asked Mr Meddle, in a voice like ice.

'Oh, please, sir, I found a great heap of snow outside

your shop, so I thought I'd better break it up and flatten it down on the pavement,' said Meddle. 'It was such a *big* heap of snow!'

'It was,' said Mr Biscuit, in a horrid sort of voice. 'I made it myself, Mr Meddle! I swept all the snow off my pavement and packed it up into a big heap to melt – and now *you've* come along and undone all my work! The snow is all over my pavement again! Come here, you meddling, interfering little man!'

But Meddle didn't go to Mr Biscuit. No, he knew better than that! He skipped off down the road as if a dog was after him.

'I'm not really getting on very well,' said Mr Meddle sadly. 'Oh, look – what a lot of snow there is outside Father Flap's house. He's an old chap, so perhaps he would like someone to dig it away for him.'

So Meddle went up to the door through the thick snow and knocked on the knocker. Father Flap opened the door. 'What is it?' he growled.

'Father Flap, let me sweep away the snow from

your garden,' said Meddle. 'I'm a good workman, I am. I'd be pleased to do it for sixpence.'

'You're not a good workman, and I don't want it done!' said Father Flap. 'I like the snow there. It looks pretty.' He slammed his door shut.

Meddle sighed. He looked up at the roof and saw that the snow lay heavily there too. 'That's really very dangerous,' he said to himself. 'That snow will slide down and bury someone if Father Flap's not careful.'

Meddle opened the letterbox flap in the front door and shouted through it. 'Hie! Shall I make your roof safe for you? There's a lot of snow there!'

There was no answer. Father Flap had gone into his warm kitchen and shut the door. Meddle stood on the snowy step and looked up at the roof.

Well, if I clear the snow from there, perhaps Father Flap will pay me for it, he thought. *If I make it all clean and push the snow off, surely he will give me sixpence.*

So he stood on the water barrel nearby and climbed up on to the roof. He clung to a chimney and began to kick at the snow with his feet to clear it from the roof.

Now Father Flap was sitting snoozing in his kitchen with Dame Flap when they suddenly heard a most peculiar noise on their roof. Of course, they had no idea that Meddle was there! They both sat up and looked at one another.

'Cats on the roof again!' said Dame Flap angrily. 'Go and shoo them off, Flap; I will *not* have cats on my roof.'

So Father Flap went to the front door and opened it. He walked out on the doorstep and looked up at the roof – and at that very moment Meddle loosened a great sheet of snow with his foot and it slid down with a swooshing sound. It fell off the roof straight on to poor Father Flap underneath! It buried him from head to foot, and he began to yell and shout.

Meddle climbed down the water barrel to see what all the noise was about. He was most astonished to hear shouts coming from the snow he had pushed off – but when he saw Father Flap's angry face suddenly looking out from the top, he guessed what had happened!

'Wait till I catch you, you meddlesome creature!' yelled Father Flap. He struggled out of the snow and ran at Meddle – but Meddle rushed away. Up the hill behind the cottage he went, up and up, hoping that Father Flap would soon be out of breath. But Father Flap was strong, and he was so angry that he meant to catch Meddle whatever happened, if he ran to the end of the world.

When Meddle got to the top of the hill he stopped. The other side was too steep to run down. Whatever was he to do? Father Flap decided that for him! He caught poor Meddle, gave him a good shaking, and then pushed him down the steep side of the hill!

Over went Meddle into the deep snow – but he didn't stop there! Dear me, no! He couldn't stop, because the hill was so steep – so down he rolled, covered with snow.

And the further he went, the more he was covered

with snow, until at last he looked like a great snowball rolling down the hill! Over and over he rolled, getting bigger every moment.

At the bottom of the hill some children were playing. When they saw the enormous snowball coming down on top of them they ran off with squeals and screams. The great snowball, with Meddle inside, rolled to the bottom of the hill, and came to a stop in the middle of the frozen pond. There it lay on the ice, quite still, with poor Meddle inside trying to shout and wriggle.

He couldn't get out and Father Flap wasn't going to run down the hill and help him, so nobody bothered at all. And there he stayed until the sun came out and began to melt the snowball.

Meddle was so pleased. Soon he would be free again – but dear me, the sun melted the ice on the pond too! And by the time that Meddle got out of the snowball the ice had turned to water, and there was Meddle splashing in the cold, half-frozen pond!

'Whatever do you want to go bathing in the pond *this* time of year for?' shouted the village policeman. 'Come on out quickly, Mr Meddle!'

Meddle came out, wet and cold. He went home and got himself a hot-water bottle and a cup of hot milk. He shook his head sadly at his old black cat who was waiting for him to give her the skin off the top of the milk.

'It's no good trying to do anything for anybody,' said Meddle. 'Not a bit of good, Pusskins.'

Well, it all depends on how you set about it, doesn't it!

One Winter
Morning

One Winter Morning

'YOU TWO children can go into the garden this morning to play,' said Mother. 'The sun is so bright, you'll enjoy it.'

'But there's still snow in the corners!' said Julia, who wanted to sit by the fire and read her book. 'It will be very cold, Mother!'

'Nonsense!' said her mother. 'You'll be warm enough in the sun – why, it's even melted the ice on the pond, look!'

So it had. When the children ran out, they found that they could no longer slide on the pond – the surface had melted. They stared down through the thinning ice to see if they could see their goldfish there.

'Yes – there they are, look!' said George. 'One, two, three, four, five – they are all there. *They* don't mind being frozen in at all.'

'I wonder if the frogs are still asleep at the bottom of the pond,' said Julia, and she gazed down into the half-frozen pond. 'I can't see any.'

'You won't! They should all be sound asleep in the mud!' said George. 'They shouldn't wake till spring is almost here, and the frost has gone away. My word – Mother is right – the sun is quite warm, and yet it's only the beginning of February!'

They got so hot playing in the winter sunshine that they wanted to take off their coats, but Mother said no, certainly not!

'But, Mother – the pond is practically *all* melted now!' said George. 'And the goldfish are as lively as anything. I bet the frogs are waking up too.'

'Oh no!' said Mother. 'It would be a very foolish frog that wakes up now – because in a day or two the bitter weather may come back again!'

But it so happened that there *was* a very foolish frog in the pond. The rays of the sun pierced through the pond waters and he stirred in his bed of mud. He awoke and gave a little wriggle. Why – surely it must be spring!

He wriggled right out of the mud and swam up to the surface, where tiny bits of ice still floated about. It felt warm in the sun. The frog croaked to wake his brothers and sisters.

They heard him and stirred too – but the wise old frog, who was the oldest in the pond, knew quite well that it wasn't time to swim about. He croaked too, and made a strange bubbling sound down in the mud – a sound that warned all the others not to stir from their muddy bed.

The frog swimming about at the surface heard the croak too, but he took no notice. He felt important, all by himself, and very clever. So he didn't go down to the mud, but stayed swimming about in the sun, enjoying himself.

The children went in to their dinner, and while they were having it, a great cloud came up and blotted out the sun. The wind began to blow from the north and suddenly it was very cold.

'Well, you just went out in time to enjoy the sun!' said Mother to the two children. 'I do believe it's going to snow now – after that warm morning too!'

So the children stayed indoors that afternoon, and when it began to snow they watched the great flakes falling down like bits of white cotton wool.

And then just about teatime George remembered that he had left his new ball out in the garden. Soon the snow would cover it and he wouldn't know where it was!

'Julia – come and help me to look for it,' he said. 'Put your coat and pixie hat on – buck up.'

So out they both went, and there was the ball near the pond, almost covered with snow already. George picked it up, and looked at the pond.

'It's freezing again,' he said. 'Soon the ice will be all over it and we shall be able to slide.'

Julia was just turning away when she caught sight of something moving slowly where the ice was forming. 'What *is* that, George?' she said.

But by this time it was getting rather dark and neither of the children could make out what the little dark thing was that was moving in the fast-forming ice, and they went indoors, shivering.

It was the foolish little frog! He had swum about merrily in the sunshine – but now the sun had gone and it was very cold. He was trying to find a warm patch in the water, for he had made up his mind that he would not go down to the mud with the others. It seemed so dull to do that, after being wakeful and happy in the sun!

So there he was, wondering what the little hard cold bits were that he kept swimming against. He did not know they were pieces of ice. As the night grew colder still, and the pond froze hard, the poor frog could no longer move his legs. He was frozen stiff in the ice!

There he stayed all night, unable to move, feeling very miserable indeed. He would die, he would never see his friends again, he would never give another croak!

Now, in the morning Julia remembered the little moving patch she had seen in the pond the day before, just as it had been getting dark, and she put on her coat and ran out to see if it was still there. She called George at once.

'George – come quickly! Look, there's a poor frog frozen into the ice! Oh, George, is he dead?'

George raced out and the two of them looked at the miserable frog, frozen hard in the ice. He didn't move at all.

'I'm going to break the ice and get him out,' said George, and he got his trowel and cracked the ice all round the frog. He lifted out the piece of ice in which the little creature was frozen and he and Julia took the frog indoors to their mother. Julia was half crying, because she couldn't bear to see the frog in the ice.

'Good gracious!' said Mother. 'Get a pail of water, George – not hot water, just ordinary – and put the frog in there, ice and all. Put the pail over in the corner of your playroom there – and the ice will soon melt. Maybe the frog will come alive – maybe he won't. You must just wait and see.'

Well, when the ice melted, the frog sank slowly to the bottom of the pail and made no movement at all – and then Julia, who had been looking into the pail every five minutes or so, gave a little cry.

'He's moving! He's alive! Look, George, his hind legs are twitching!'

So they were – and before another hour had passed, the foolish little frog was swimming merrily about the pail, wondering what had happened to him. What a narrow escape he had had!

The children were very pleased. 'Can we keep him

in the pail here till the frost and ice have gone – and then put him back into the pond?' asked Julia. Mother nodded.

'Yes. It's the only thing to do! But don't expect to make a pet of him, because frogs don't make good pets. And, George – put a bit of wood on the top of the water in the pail – he will like to sit there at times – and as soon as the pond unfreezes a little, pick some of the waterweed for the pail.'

The frog rather liked his pail and bit of wood. But after a day or two he hopped right off the wood and on to the floor and explored the playroom thoroughly. He leapt here and he leapt there, and when the children came in from school, there he was, sitting calmly on the head of a small bear on wheels that the children had had for years!

He leapt high into the air as soon as he saw the children, and jumped on his long hind legs to meet them. He knew them well by now and was not at all afraid of them.

'Croak!' he said. 'CROAK!'

'Oh – you've found your voice!' said Julia, delighted. 'Isn't it a loud one, George! Let's call him Croak, shall we? I do believe he *is* going to be a pet!'

So he was! Although he made the pail his home, and swam there a good deal, he was always out and about the playroom. Once he got into the dolls' house and Julia gave a sudden shout when she saw him looking out of the front door.

'Croak! You do look funny there! Don't you frighten my tiny dolls now!'

'*Crrrrrroak!*' said Croak, and hopped out to her. He sat down on her foot. He liked this girl. '*Crrrrrrrrroak!*' He had a fine big voice now, and he liked using it.

His friends were still asleep at the bottom of the pond, for the weather was icy cold – but Croak was always wide awake and very cheerful. Mother laughed to hear him croaking away to himself when the children were at school!

And then, one evening when the two children

were asleep in bed, and Daddy and Mother were watching the television programme downstairs with a friend, something happened.

The window in the playroom was softly slid up from the bottom, and a torch was flashed quickly on and off. Then a low voice said, 'It's all right, Jim. The grown-ups are watching television downstairs and the kids are in bed. We can get in here and take what we want. No noise now!'

Two youths climbed quietly in at the window and stood in the dark listening. One of them switched on his torch and flashed it around the room.

The light disturbed Croak the frog. He was in the pail, dozing on the bit of wood at the top of the water. He gave a loud croak when the light shone out.

'CROAK!'

'What was that?' said Jim, startled. 'It sounded over in that corner.'

The two stood quite still – and then they heard a splash and a little thud. That was Croak jumping out of the pail on to the linoleum.

'Sh!' whispered Jim. 'Joe – did you hear that?' The two lads stood and listened again.

'*Cr-r-r-r-r-roak*!' said Croak, in his very best voice, and the youths jumped, because it sounded so near. That wasn't surprising, as Croak had leapt up on to a nearby chair.

'It – it sounds like a frog!' whispered Jim.

'Don't be daft!' said Joe. 'Frogs live in ponds not houses. Come on – let's go to a bedroom and see what we can find. We're on the first floor, so . . .'

'*Cr-r-r-roak*!' That was Croak again, thinking that these people must be George and Julia come to see him. He leapt on to Joe's foot, landing with a little bump.

'OW!' said Joe, startled, and clutched at Jim.

'Ooooh!' said Jim, alarmed at Joe's sudden grab at him. 'What is it?'

'Something's on my foot,' said Joe. 'Here, I don't like this!' He shone his torch down, but by that time

Croak had leapt off his foot and was crouched on the floor.

'You're potty!' said Jim. 'Come on – let's go and find a bedroom. The television is still on downstairs. I can hear it.'

They opened the playroom door quietly and went into the passage. Croak was thrilled. He had never been out of the room, because the children carefully kept it shut. He leapt after the two lads. They came to the children's room and heard them breathing, fast asleep, so they went on to the next one.

But Croak slipped into the children's room. He sensed that Julia and George were there. He would find Julia. He liked her so very much. He leapt on to a little bedside table – and then on to Julia's pillow. Yes – this was Julia.

'CROAK!' he said, right in her ear, and she awoke at once and sat up.

'Why – it's you, Croak!' she said in astonishment. 'You naughty little frog! The cat will get you if you leave the playroom. How did you get out? I *know* I shut the door!'

She picked up the frog gently, got out of bed and padded to the door – but as soon as she was on the landing, she stopped still. Someone was in her mother's bedroom – someone with a torch – opening drawers! Who was it?

Holding Croak still in her hand, the little girl sped softly down the stairs to the sitting room where her mother and father and a friend were watching television.

'Daddy! There's someone in your room upstairs,' panted Julia, and in a trice Daddy and his friend shot upstairs at top speed!

What a shock for the two lads, Joe and Jim! They found themselves held tightly by their coat collars and hauled downstairs very firmly indeed. Mother rang up the police – and Julia watched open-mouthed. What a thing to happen! George had been awakened by the scuffling and shouting, and had come downstairs too.

He saw Croak in Julia's hand and was astonished. 'Why have you got *him*?' he said.

'He came and croaked in my ear when I was asleep!' said Julia. 'And I awoke and found him and went to put him back in his pail – and I saw these horrid burglars in Mummy's room.'

'Gosh!' said Joe, staring at the frog. 'So it *was* a frog we heard. It jumped on my foot, and ...'

'CROAK!' said Croak, proudly. 'CROAK!'

Just then the police came, and Joe and Jim were hustled away. Daddy shut the front door after them and came back to the sitting room. He was smiling.

'Well – this is good enough to make into a story. "Frog saves household from burglars!" Is that the little frog you saved from being frozen in the ice, children?'

'Yes,' said Julia, tickling Croak under the chin. 'And now he's saved *us* from something unpleasant. Croak, we hope you shall live in our pond for always – you're a hero!'

So Croak is still with George and Julia. In the summer and autumn he lives in their garden and catches flies – and in the cold weather he lives in the pond. When Julia and George come running into the garden and call 'Croak!' he leaps out from under his bush or out of his patch of grass, and sits on Julia's foot.

'It was a very good thing we saved you from freezing to death in the ice, Croak,' Julia often says to him. And he always makes exactly the same answer, of course!

'*Cr-r-r-r-r-roak!*'

Is There Anything Particular You Want?

Is There Anything
Particular You Want?

'JANIE, GO and sweep the snow from the front door down to the gate, will you?' asked Granny.

Oh dear! thought Janie, *just as I was going to read my book and eat my sweets! Bother! But I suppose Granny can't do it herself.*

She stood up and Granny saw her rather cross face.

'I'll give you sixpence towards your new pair of skates if you'll do it, Janie,' she said. 'I can't do it because of my bad leg.'

'Oh, Granny – I'll do it for *nothing*!' said Janie. 'Anyway, the skates cost such a lot of money that sixpence won't help me get them before this cold spell has gone! I'll have to wait another year, I'm afraid.'

There was skating on the Big Pond that winter, and Janie had borrowed a pair of skates and had found that she could skate very well for a beginner – and now more than anything else she wanted a pair of skates of her own! What a pity they cost so much money!

She put on her coat, took the broom and out she went to the front door and began to sweep the snow away. Goodness, how deep it was! No wonder the postman had grumbled about it this morning when he had brought the letters.

Janie swept and swept, and her arms soon grew tired. What a long front path it seemed when she was sweeping it – though it seemed short enough when she ran down to the gate each day.

Sweeeeep, sweeeeep, sweeeeep! The broom made a clear path and soon people would be able to walk from the gate to the front door easily. The broom suddenly uncovered something that made a little clatter. It shone, and Janie bent down to look at it.

'Why – it's a brooch!' she said. 'What a pretty one! Perhaps it's Granny's, though I've never seen it before. I'll take it indoors when I've finished and ask her if it's hers.'

So she showed Granny the brooch as soon as she had finished sweeping. 'Is it yours, Granny?' she asked. 'I found it under the snow on the front path. Did you drop it when you went out?'

'I haven't been out since the snow fell,' said Granny, and took the brooch. 'Oh – what a beauty! I do wonder who has lost it? Let me see – who came here during the last two or three days?'

They couldn't think of *anyone* they knew who might have come to the house wearing such a lovely brooch.

'There's only that lady who came and asked us where Red Chimney House was,' said Janie, remembering. '*She* might have dropped it – but we don't know who she was or where she lives!'

'You must take it to the police station, Janie dear,'

said Granny. 'We can't keep it here.'

'Oh, Granny – I don't want to go into the police station,' said Janie. 'I'd be afraid. I wouldn't know what to say.'

'Well – I'd better get my coat on and hobble through the snow myself,' said Granny. 'This is really a very valuable brooch, Janie – and someone must be very worried about it.'

'No – don't get your coat, Granny,' said Janie. 'I'll go – though really and truly I'm afraid, and I'm sure I shall turn and run down the steps if the policemen ask me too many questions.'

'They won't,' said Granny. 'Well, go, dear – and don't be too long.'

So off went Janie with the lovely brooch held safely in an empty matchbox. She felt very nervous when she walked up the police station steps and went in at the door. A big policeman was sitting at a table inside.

'Well?' he said, with a broad smile. 'And what do

you want? Come to give yourself up for committing a burglary?'

That made Janie laugh. 'Oh no!' she said. 'I just came to bring you a brooch I found when I was sweeping away the snow from our front door today. Here it is.'

The policeman emptied it out of the matchbox and then gave a low whistle.

He picked up the brooch and looked at it this way and that, and then he took a printed sheet of paper and read it to himself, and looked at the brooch again. Janie watched him, puzzled. At last he put the brooch down and looked at her.

'Well, well, well!' he said. 'Now tell me – is there anything in particular that you are simply *longing* to have? A new doll? A set of books? A new dress?'

Janie stared in astonishment. Whatever did he mean?

'Well – the only thing I *really* want is a pair of skates!' she said. 'Why?'

'Look at this,' said the policeman and pushed across

to her the sheet of paper he had been reading. Janie read it. Goodness! It described the brooch she had found – described it exactly – three diamonds at the top, one ruby in the centre, the whole set in small pearls, with a gold pin at the back – and it had been lost by Lady Green-Acres, who was offering... goodness, this couldn't be true – offering FIVE POUNDS to anyone who found the brooch and brought it back.

'There you are!' said the policeman with his broad smile. 'That's why I said to you – is there anything particular you want? You said you'd found the brooch when you were sweeping the snow away from your granny's front door – so you'll have the five pounds to spend on anything you like!'

Janie sped back to Granny as if she had wings on her feet. Oh what a good thing Granny had asked her to sweep away the snow – and what a *very* good thing she had done it at once! Five whole pounds! That meant skates at once – and it meant a present for dear Granny too. The biggest bowl of bulbs she could buy in the flower shop, because she liked those so much.

If only, only the ice doesn't melt before I get the five pounds and buy my skates! thought Janie, as she rushed indoors to find Granny.

Don't worry, Janie – the ice will last another three weeks, and you'll get your reward tomorrow – and long before the three weeks is up you'll be the best little skater on the Big Pond!

Is there anything particular *you* want? Well, I hope you'll be as lucky as Janie – and get it!

Happy New Year!

Happy New Year!

'TODAY IS the last day of the old year,' said Mummy to Paddy. 'Tomorrow the New Year comes in. You must go round to Granny and wish her a Happy New Year.'

'What do I say to her?' said Paddy. 'Just, "A Happy New Year"?'

'Yes – just that,' said Mummy. 'That's what everyone says on New Year's Day.'

'I shall say it to the gardener, and to the baker and to the milkman,' said Paddy. 'I'd better tell Meg to say it too, hadn't I?'

'Oh, Meg's too little,' said Mummy. 'She wouldn't

understand what Happy New Year means. She's only four years old – she hardly knows what a year *is*!'

'It's twelve months, isn't it?' said Paddy, 'and it's three hundred and sixty-five days. It's a long, long time.'

He went to find Meg. 'Meggy,' he said, 'tomorrow you have to say "Happy New Year!" to everyone. So don't forget.'

Meg thought that he said, 'Happy New *Ear*' and she was very surprised.

'I don't want a new ear,' she said. 'I like the ones I've got.'

'Don't be silly,' said Paddy. 'You'll hear me saying "Happy New Year" to everyone. You must too. I'm going to say it to the baker and the milkman, and . . .'

'But they don't want new ears,' said Meg, solemnly. 'I don't want to say it to them. I shall just say it to my toys.'

'All right –you say it to *them*!' said Paddy, and went off to play. Meggy began to play with her toys, muttering softly to herself.

'Happy new ear! Happy new ear! Oh, Teddy, you've only one ear left – *you* want a happy new ear, don't you? And Monkey, one of your ears is falling off. Did you know?'

She looked at her bear and her monkey and thought that they looked back rather sadly at her. She hugged them.

'I'll *get* you a happy new ear, Teddy,' she said. 'And I'll sew Monkey's on again, then *he'll* have a happy new ear too!'

Just then the cat came into the playroom and walked over to Meggy, purring. Meg stroked him. A few weeks back he had been in a fight and one of his ears was badly bitten.

'I wish I could get *you* a new ear too, Puss-Cat,' said Meg. 'I'll just have to wish you one tomorrow!'

Next day was New Year's Day, but Meg wouldn't wish Mummy a Happy New Year. 'No,' she said. 'I like your old ears, Mummy. You mustn't have new ones.'

331

'What *is* the child chattering about now?' said Mummy. 'And what are you doing with a needle and cotton, Meggy? You can't sew! Did you take them out of my workbasket?'

'Yes – I'm giving Teddy a happy new ear,' said Meg, and she held up a little bit of brown felt she had taken from the basket too. Mummy thought she said 'A Happy New Year,' and she laughed. 'You don't *give* people a Happy New Year, you just wish them one,' she said.

Meggy went over to her bear, and took him on her knee. She tried her best to sew on the new ear she had got for him – but all that happened was that she pricked her finger badly. She began to yell.

'Oh! I'm bleeding! Look at my blood! Oh, I've got such a lot of blood on my finger, look!'

Mummy ran to comfort her. 'Let *me* put on Teddy's new ear,' she said, and she sewed it on beautifully.

'Now sew Monkey's ear on, please,' said Meg. 'He's to have a happy new ear, too. I wish we could give Puss-Cat a new ear as well – one of his is bitten.'

'Oh, you funny little thing!' cried Mummy. 'You think we're wishing everyone a Happy New *Ear*, don't you! Meggy, darling – it isn't *ears* we're wishing people today, it's *years*! Can't you hear the difference?'

'Not very well,' said Meggy. 'What is a year?'

'You're too little to know,' said Mummy. 'Paddy, look here – our Meggy is giving Teddy and Monkey happy new ears – *do* look!'

'Well, Meggy – I'm quite sure Monkey and Teddy will have a very happy New Year with their lovely new ears!' said Paddy, laughing. He bent down and kissed his small sister. 'And a Happy New Year to you too!'

'I don't want one,' said Meggy. 'I like my own ears. I told you that before. They're very, very good ears – they hear everything. But I'm glad Teddy's got a happy new ear – he's smiling, look!'

So he was, and I don't wonder. Anyone would smile at Meggy!

When Mr
Pink-Whistle Met
the Twins

When Mr Pink-Whistle Met the Twins

MR PINK-WHISTLE met the twins in rather a peculiar way. He was on his way to Mr Bong's Christmas party, and as he was a little late, he was in a great hurry. Sooty, his cat, was with him, because he had been invited too, and they were both going down the street as fast as they could.

'We really must hurry,' said Mr Pink-Whistle, hurrying round the corner at top speed. BUMP! They ran straight into two children, a boy and a girl, and knocked them both right over. Mr Pink-Whistle sat down with a bump, and Sooty rolled into the gutter! Everyone was most surprised.

'Oooh,' said the children.

'Good gracious!' said Pink-Whistle and Sooty gave a yowl. Pink-Whistle hurried to pick up the two children and was upset to see tears pouring down the little girl's cheek.

'Have I hurt you?' he said. 'Oh dear – don't cry so! I'm very, very sorry to have bumped you like that. It was all my fault – I was in such a hurry.'

'She's not crying because you knocked her over,' said the boy, dusting his sister's coat down with his hand. 'She's upset about something else.'

'Is she? Why, what's the matter?' asked Pink-Whistle. 'You don't either of you look very happy!'

'Well – we don't *feel* very happy!' said the boy. 'You see, today we were to have our Christmas party and everything was ready – and then suddenly our granny was taken ill and Mummy had to rush to her house to look after her. So we can't have our party.'

'And we're running to tell our friends not to come,' said the girl, rubbing her eyes. 'I'm a baby to cry – but

I'm *so* disappointed. We were going to have a conjurer, and we've had to tell *him* not to come too.'

'What a dreadful thing to happen!' said kind old Pink-Whistle. 'I hope your granny will soon be well. I know how disappointed *I* would feel – I'm just *going* to a party!'

'Are you?' said the boy. 'And the cat too?'

'Oh, yes. He's been asked as well,' said Pink-Whistle. 'The funny thing is – it's a conjurer who's giving the party I'm going to! At least – he's a magician, you know – an enchanter.'

The twins stared at him in wonder. What did this funny little man mean? Then the boy saw his pointed ears and caught hold of his sister's arm in excitement.

'Belinda!' he said. 'Look – he must be Mr Pink-Whistle. *You* know – we've read about him! He's the little man who goes about the world putting wrong things right!'

Belinda stopped crying at once and stared in delight. Mr Pink-Whistle nodded.

'Yes. Pink-Whistle's my name,' he said. 'What are *your* names? You're twins, of course?'

'Yes. I'm Benny and she's Belinda,' said the boy, red with excitement. 'Have you put any wrong things right lately, Mr Pink-Whistle?'

'Not since last week,' said Pink-Whistle, 'but I'm going to put something right this very afternoon!'

'How? Tell us what it is!' said Belinda, quite forgetting to cry.

'I'm going to take you to the party *I'm* going to!' said Pink-Whistle. 'And all the other children too! Things went very wrong for you this afternoon, didn't they? Well, I can put them right. Mr Bong, my friend, will be delighted to see you all!'

'But – but will he have enough to eat if we bring about twelve children with us?' said Benny, wondering if he was in a dream.

'My dear boy – haven't I told you he is a *magician*?' said Pink-Whistle. 'One of the very finest I know too. Now, listen, take Sooty with you and go round to all your friends and ask them to come to Mr Bong's party. Sooty will take you all to Mr Bong's house – and I'll go straight there to warn him I'm bringing a lot more guests! We'll all have a wonderful time!'

The twins could hardly believe their ears. To think that such a thing could happen to *them*? They set off at once with Sooty, and goodness me, how amazed all their friends were to hear their news! Most of the children were already dressed, ready to go to the twins' party, and it wasn't long before Benny and Belinda had collected them all and, with Sooty guiding them, were on their way to Mr Bong's.

They came to a little lane they knew, that led down to the woods – but before they reached the woods, Sooty turned down a trim little path which the children had never seen before.

'You can only see it today because Mr Bong has arranged for it to be here,' explained Sooty. 'It's a shortcut to his house.'

And suddenly, in front of them, was Mr Bong's

house! It was really more like a small castle, with towers and turrets – and about a hundred steps leading up to a front door that was just below the roof. How queer!

'Isn't it exciting!' whispered Belinda to Benny. 'Fancy us not knowing this queer little castle was anywhere near our town!'

Soon they were up the steps and in at the front door. Mr Pink-Whistle was there to take them in. They looked around for Mr Bong, but he wasn't there.

'He's coming in a short while,' said Pink-Whistle. 'Do take off your things. That's right. Now, what are your names? Mr Bong is so pleased you are coming. He has just gone to fetch his own friends.'

The children took off their things and Sooty scuttled away with all the coats and cloaks. Then suddenly there came the sound of a drum being beaten – *Bom-bom-BOM*! Then a voice cried, 'Here comes Bong, the mighty enchanter Bong! Make way for Bong!'

The children stared at a great door which had suddenly appeared in the wall. It glittered and shone, and then very slowly it opened.

Through it came a wonderful figure, in a great cloak that glowed like fire. He had a long beard and eyes that shone like lamps. He smiled at all the children.

'Welcome!' he said. 'Welcome to my party! Please be friends with my own guests!' He waved his great, shining wand and from behind him came the guests he had been to fetch.

What a mixture they were! 'That's Mr Whiskers, a brownie – he's a hundred years old today,' whispered Pink-Whistle to the children, as a little man scampered out. 'And that's Silky, a fairy from the Faraway Tree. Isn't she lovely? And that's Moonface – he's from the Faraway Tree too.'

'But we know them all!' cried Benny in delight. 'We've read about them in our books! Oh – and there's the old Saucepan Man! Saucepan, Saucepan, can you

343

hear me or are you deaf today?'

The Saucepan Man beamed round in delight. 'I didn't know there were to be children here!' he said, and danced a ridiculous dance, so that all his pans and kettles clanged together and made a queer little tune.

Then a rabbit came in – but what a rabbit! He was dressed very smartly and grinned round wickedly at everyone.

'Brer Rabbit! Oh, *you've* come too!' shouted the children and ran to him at once.

'Be careful he doesn't play a trick on you,' said Pink-Whistle. 'Look – here are a bunch of pixies. They will love to play with you. What about beginning with "Nuts in May"? Then if others come in late, they can easily join in.'

So they began to play 'Here We Come Gathering Nuts in May' and when Mr Pink-Whistle and Mr Bong were chosen to try and pull one another across the line, you should have heard the screams of laughter. In the end Mr Bong won because he poked his wand at Pink-Whistle, and made him only half his size – and then pulled him over easily! More brownies came in – and dear me, who was this?

'Big-Ears! It's Big-Ears!' shouted the children and ran to the plump little brownie, who stood beaming round at them. 'Where's Noddy? Did you bring him, Big-Ears?'

'No. I'm afraid not. He's taking all the Noah's ark animals to a party,' said Big-Ears. 'I say, Mr Bong – is it teatime yet? I'm hungry!'

'Yes, yes – we were just waiting for you!' said Mr Bong. 'Sit down at the table, do!'

There was a long table at one end of the room – but there was no food on it at all, only plates and glasses. Everyone sat down.

'Do begin!' said Mr Bong. 'Help yourselves!'

'But there's nothing to eat!' said Benny in surprise. Pink-Whistle nudged his arm. 'Do what the others are doing,' he said. 'Watch Big-Ears and Silky.'

Benny watched. Big-Ears was calling out all kinds

of things, holding out his empty hands. 'Egg sandwiches!' he cried. 'Chocolate eclairs! Pink and yellow jelly! Ice cream – a large one! A glass of iced lemonade!'

And into his hands popped everything he asked for – just like that! Benny stared and stared. 'Good gracious – there's his glass of lemonade!' he said. 'It looked as if Big-Ears took it right out of the air! Well – I'll do the same!'

And soon all the children were calling out what they wanted. 'Jam tarts!', 'Doughnuts!', 'Tomato sandwiches!', 'A nice ripe peach!', 'Jelly!', 'Trifle!', 'Fruit salad!'

The table was soon loaded with all kinds of good things to eat. Pink-Whistle wasn't very pleased with Sooty, who had called out for fish and got two rather smelly kippers in front of him.

'Sooty – I've told you before not to ask for fish at these parties,' said Pink-Whistle in a whisper. 'Take it under the table, for goodness' sake. It smells.'

Tea took rather a long time because everyone had rather a lot to eat. Afterwards the children begged Mr Bong to do some magic.

'Shall I spirit you to the moon and back?' he asked with a twinkle in his eye. 'Shall I give you tails like Sooty's? Or would you like wings to fly with?'

'Wings! Wings!' shouted the children in excitement. They each had to go up to Mr Bong and be touched on the back by his magic wand – and wings sprouted there, some like the wings of a butterfly and some like a bird's. The air was full of flying children, shouting and laughing in joy.

'You may keep your wings to fly home on,' said Mr Bong. 'But as soon as you fly down to your own doorstep, they will disappear – so make the most of them!'

The magic that the enchanter could do was amazing. He filled the air with the singing of birds – but not a bird was to be seen! He called a rainbow down from the skies – and it slid in at the window, a shimmering, curving bow, so bright that the children could hardly look at it.

Mr Bong took a pair of scissors and snipped pieces from the rainbow, and gave them to the girls. 'For you – and you – and you,' he said, 'to make a new party dress!'

He waved his wand and a small tree grew in the room – a tree that budded as they watched. The buds broke into flowers, which changed into a most peculiar fruit, rather like big brown pears, each with a stalk.

'Pick one each, boys,' said Mr Bong. 'You will see what kind of a tree this is then!' So the boys went to pick the strange fruits – and behold, they were spinning tops and the stalks were the tops' sturdy legs!

'Throw them on the floor,' said Mr Bong, and down on the floor went the tops – and there they spun themselves so fast that they could hardly be seen!

'I wish I could grow a top tree in our garden,' said Benny. 'These are the best spinning tops I've ever seen!'

Then Mr Bong grew a balloon bush that budded and then flowered into enormous coloured balloons – and he grew a cracker tree whose fruits were real crackers. Pop, bang, pop they went, when the children pulled them. And what wonderful things fell out of them! There was no end to them.

At last it was time to go. 'You can all fly home on your wings,' said Pink-Whistle. 'Just as Mr Bong said! Take your presents with you – the things out of the crackers, the tops and the snippets of rainbow. And now – what about a cheer for kind Mr Bong who helped me once more to put a wrong thing right!'

'Hip-hip-hip-HURRAH!' shouted the children and everyone else. 'Hip-hip-hip-HURRAH!' And so loudly did they shout that the little castle trembled and shook – and then it vanished into smoke that blew about like a silver mist!

But the children didn't mind! They flew up into the air on their wings, eager to get home and tell their mothers all about the wonderful party. How marvellous to fly like a bird! Pink-Whistle watched them all go, with Sooty beside him. He waved happily.

'I hope they remember that their wings will disappear when they arrive home,' he said. 'What a time we've had, Sooty – I always enjoy Mr Bong's parties. Dear me – I do hope you will wash your whiskers as soon as you get home, Sooty. You still smell of those kippers!'

Goodbye, Pink-Whistle – and how I hope that if anything goes wrong with me, I shall do as the twins did – bump into you round the next corner!

A Boy in a Thousand!

A Boy in a Thousand!

'WELL – WHAT did you do at school this morning?' asked Mummy, when Jack came home to his dinner.

'We had a jolly nice lesson on how to make a bird table,' said Jack. 'And I'm going to make one. I shall spread it with lots of food every day!'

'And where are you going to get this "lots of food"?' asked his mother.

'Well, our teacher said that we were to have a cardboard carton of some sort, and give it to our mothers and ask them if they'd put into it all the household scraps,' said Jack. 'You know, Mummy – bits of bread left over, or potatoes – that sort of thing.'

'Now you know I give most of our scraps to the chickens for food,' said his mother. 'And Tinker the dog gobbles up the rest!'

'Then I shall take a carton round to the neighbours,' said Jack. 'I'm sure they'll help me. Mummy, it would be *fun* to have a bird table and watch the birds come down and feed. I bet I'd tame a robin or two!'

'Here's an empty cream carton then,' said his mother, and Jack took it at once.

'I'll pop round here and there after I've had my dinner,' he said. And in about half an hour off he went with the little empty carton. He knocked at Mrs Jones's door and told her about the bird table he planned to make, and the food he was going to collect for the birds.

'Well now, that's a really good idea,' said Mrs Jones. 'This bitter weather the birds can't find much to eat, especially since it's been snowing so hard. Let me see what I've got in the way of bits.'

She half filled Jack's carton with bread and bacon

rind. He was very pleased. He went next door to Mr
Hollins. But Mr Hollins wasn't so kind. 'What! Feed
the birds that steal my cherries every summer?' he
said. 'I should think not!'

'But you have so many cherries, can't you spare
them a *few* in summer?' said Jack. Bang! The door was
shut. Jack went off to Miss Lacy's.

'A bird table! Now that sounds a fine idea!' said
Miss Lacy. 'Yes, of course I'll save my bits for you
each day. In fact I could fill a whole carton of bits,
you know, because we're a big household here. Why
don't you leave me your carton to fill?'

Before long Jack had quite a round of people ready
to save him their bits. He decided that it would be
easier to give them each an empty carton, and then to
go around with his seaside pail and empty them all
each morning into the pail.

He made a fine bird table. It only took him one
hour! Harry leant over the fence and watched him.
'Why! All you did was to take your mother's old

broom handle, dig a hole in the ground and ram it in – and then you nailed that flat board on the top of it – and then found some twigs and nailed them at the back! It looks fine, Jack. What food are you going to put on it?'

'The food I collect from all the neighbours, Harry,' said Jack. 'You come in and look inside this pail of mine – the birds are going to get a fine feast!'

Harry came in to look. 'Gracious! What a hotch-potch of food – potatoes, bits of somebody's rice pudding, bread, stale cake, bacon rinds, fat – and what's this – a bone? Hey, are you going to feed dogs too?'

Jack laughed. 'No! I'm going to hang that down from the edge of the table for the tits and starlings to peck at. And do you know what I'm spending my Saturday money on this week?'

'No. What?' asked Harry, digging a stick about in the pail to see what else he could find there.

'Half a pound of monkey nuts – peanuts you know,'

said Jack. 'The tits go mad over them! I shall thread them on a string and hang them from the edge of the table too.'

In two days all the birds in the district had discovered Jack's bird table, and it was full from morning to night. The robin was the very first one down on his table, pecking at some bread. When he saw Jack looking out of the window, he put his head on one side, swelled out his lovely red breast, and sang a loud little song.

'Well, that's a very nice way of saying thank you,' said Jack. He watched the other birds come down – the big blackbird, hungry for a potato; the starlings, quarrelsome and amusing, pushing each other, anxious to get their share; the big thrush with his freckled breast and the many small sparrows, hungry and bold.

'And here come the tits!' he said, as a big great tit flew down, brilliant in green and yellow, with a satiny black head. 'And here are the blue tits with their pretty blue caps – I thought they'd soon find the nuts! Mummy, come here – watch that blue tit swinging upside down on my string of nuts!'

The neighbours soon got to know Jack very well indeed, for he appeared regularly every day with his pail, to empty their 'bird food' into it from the cartons he had left at each house. Sometimes when they came home from shopping they leaned over the fence to watch the birds on his table in the garden. There was often quite a little crowd of people there!

'I wouldn't mind having a bird table myself,' said Mrs Peters, one day. 'Those tits are enough to make anyone laugh – why, they're proper little acrobats!'

'Well, I'll make you one if you like,' said Jack. 'I'll go round to the carpenter and pick up a stick or pole of some sort for a leg, and a bit of board and some more nails.'

'I'll pay you for making it,' said Mrs Peters. 'Would half-a-crown do?'

'Ooh yes!' said Jack, delighted. 'I'm saving up

for my mother's birthday, but I haven't got very much yet. I'll set to work tomorrow for you – it's a Saturday.'

On Sunday morning Jack took a fine bird table round to Mrs Peters. He had got an old rake handle from the carpenter for twopence and had sawn it in half. There – that would do for *two* bird tables, one for Mrs Peters, and one for anyone else who might want one. The carpenter had given him the bottom out of an old box for nothing, and a handful of nails.

Mrs Peters was delighted with the bird table, and told everyone about it. 'You should just see the way the birds flock down!' she said. 'My, it's as good as a pantomime to watch them. Now I wonder if Jack could make something of the kind for poor old Mrs Hughes, who lives at the top of our building and can never get out at all? It would be something for her to watch – she can't see much but walls and chimneys from her window!'

As soon as Jack was told about Mrs Hughes

he climbed all the hundred-and-one steps to her tiny two-roomed flat at the top of the big building. Mrs Hughes was surprised to see a small boy opening her door, when she called, 'Come in'.

He saw a very little old lady lying on a couch by the window. She smiled at him. 'Well, who are you? I couldn't get up to open the door for you because I can hardly walk. It's nice to see you – I'm so lonely up here all by myself.'

'I'm Jack Milner and I make bird tables,' said the boy. 'I just wondered if you'd like one for your windowsill – you've no idea how interesting it is to watch birds gobbling up all kinds of food – quarrelling, and pushing each other about, and hanging upside down to peck nuts, and . . .'

'Oh yes, I know all about birds!' said Mrs Hughes. 'I used to live in the country and I loved them. I miss them so much now. Could you *really* make a bird table for my windowsill? I should feel so happy again if I could watch the birds – and I've always bits of food left over – I could put a saucer of water out too.'

Jack went to the window. Alas, there was no windowsill – just a tiny ledge not big enough to hold even a small bird table. 'I know what I could do!' he said. 'If you don't mind my driving a big nail in each side of the wooden window frame, I could hang a narrow board where your sill *ought* to be, and you could put food and water on that.'

'I don't know why you should be so kind to me!' said the old lady. 'Do you know you're the first person I've seen for two weeks? Nobody wants to climb up all the steps to my two rooms! Please, please do put up this bird table you're talking about. If I haven't any friends to climb the stairs, I'll soon have some who can *fly* to me!'

Jack was as good as his word. He soon drove in a couple of stout nails. He took a narrow board and made two holes in it, one at each end, and threaded rope through, knotting it under the holes. Then he twisted the other ends of the rope round the nails and tied them there.

'There's your bird table!' he said. 'I'll put out a saucer of water for you – and some crumbs, or whatever you've got. And look, here's a string of peanuts I've threaded ready for you. I'll hang those down from one of the nails.'

As soon as he had finished his job, two tits were hanging on the nuts, and a sparrow was on the board where crumbs were spread. Mrs Hughes was delighted. 'Could you pull my sofa nearer to the window?' she begged. 'Oh, I *am* going to enjoy myself today! Do you think I'll be able to tame any of the birds?'

'Well, I've tamed my robin now,' said Jack. 'He flies on to my hand and takes things from my fingers. You see if you can't tame a robin too. There – that's all finished. I'll come and see how you're getting on with the birds tomorrow.'

'Wait – how much do I owe you for this?' asked Mrs Hughes, getting a purse out from under her cushion. 'I know children expect to be paid for every single thing nowadays!'

'I'm not charging you anything,' said Jack. 'I do charge a bit when I get *orders* from people for a bird table, because I'm saving up for my mother's birthday. But I'm not going to charge *you* a penny. I wouldn't dream of it.'

And away he went, leaving the old lady feeling that the world wasn't such a lonely, unkind place after all!

When Jack told his mother what he had done and how grateful the old lady had been, she didn't say anything for a minute or two. Jack looked at her. 'Are you cross, Mummy?' he said. 'You didn't *mind* my going, did you – honestly she's such a poor, *lonely* old lady.'

'Cross? No – I'm feeling rather ashamed of myself,' said his mother. 'What am I and the neighbours thinking about to let a poor old thing like that lie on her sofa and be lonely for weeks on end? I shall go and see her tomorrow and take her some chocolates.

I feel rather proud of you, Jack!'

Before long, everyone heard about Jack's bird table for old Mrs Hughes – and they heard, too, that it was full of birds all day long, and that the old lady was no longer lonely and bored. She had her birds now – *her* birds, her own small visitors. She had a robin that flew into the room and pecked crumbs off the table. She had three blue tits that swung upside down on the string of nuts and made her laugh till she cried with their antics.

She had other visitors, too. Jack's mother went to see her, and told the neighbours about her, so that they too climbed the many stairs, taking little gifts – a book to read, a magazine, a few flowers. Old Mrs Hughes couldn't get over it all!

'Such kindness!' she said. 'And all because a strange little boy suddenly appeared and put up that bird table for me! He's a boy in a thousand. I just hope he gets all the money he wants to buy his mother's birthday present. He told me that's the reason for all his work in making bird tables.'

Well, Jack did get all the money he wanted. By the time his mother's birthday arrived, he had put up so many bird tables for people that he had over a pound in his savings box, and he went out proudly to spend it. A whole pound!

He spent it on a beautiful brooch, and wrapped the little box up carefully in gay paper. He watched his mother undo it on her birthday morning. She gasped in delight and stared at it in amazement.

'But *Jack!* It's beautiful! Oh, I did so want a brooch like this, because I lost my other nice one, you know! Jack, how *did* you manage to get the money for it?'

'Aha – I had some help!' said Jack. 'It was all because of the sparrows and robins and starlings and tits, Mummy. I made bird tables for them – and that's how I got the money.'

Well, who would have thought that because a boy called Jack knew how to make bird tables, hundreds of birds are well fed this winter, many people have learnt to love them, an old lady has plenty of friends to visit her – and his mother proudly wears the most beautiful brooch she has ever had.

I really feel I'll have to go straight out and make a bird table myself!

Acknowledgments

All efforts have been made to seek necessary permissions.

The stories in this publication first appeared in the following publications:

'A Little Snow House' first appeared in *Sunday Graphic*, No. 1658, January 12, 1947

'It's Really True!' first appeared in *Sunny Stories*, No. 320, 1944

'The Sparrow Children' first appeared in *Sunny Stories*, No. 163, 1940

'A Peep Into the Magic Mirror' first appeared in *Sunny Stories*, No. 447, 1949

'Mr Stamp-About Loses His Temper' first appeared in *Sunny Stories*, No. 448, 1949

'Big-Foot Is Very Clever' first appeared in *Sunday Mail*, No. 1894, 1945

'Two Good Turns' first appeared in *Sunny Stories*, No. 421, 1948

'Bad Luck, Wily Weasel!' first appeared in *You*, No. 3, 1951

'I Dare You To!' first appeared in *Sunny Stories*, No. 371, 1946

'The Hungry Little Robin' first appeared in *Sunny Stories*, No. 159, 1940

'He Was Much Too Clever!' first appeared in *Sunny Stories*, No. 146, 1939

'Mr Pink-Whistle Comes Along' first appeared in *Sunny Stories*, No. 521, 1951

'She Never Could Remember' first appeared in *Sunny Stories*, No. 469, 1949

'The Swallow Fairy' first appeared in *Sunny Stories*, No. 365, 1945

'Father Time and His Pattern Book' first appeared in *Sunny Stories*, No. 207, 1940

'Mr Snoop's Carrots' first appeared in *Sunny Stories*, No. 345, 1945

'A Jolly Thing to Do!' first appeared in *Sunny Stories*, No. 365, 1945

'Heyho and the North Wind' first appeared in *Sunny Stories*, No. 96, 1930

'Scallywag's Mistake' first appeared in *Sunny Stories*, No. 526, 1952

'The Proud Fir Tree' first appeared in *Sunny Stories*, No. 264, 1942

'The Winter Wide-Awakes' first appeared in *Tales of Green Hedges*, 1946

'Mr Twiddle and the Snowman' first appeared in *Sunny Stories*, No. 108, 1939

'What a Good Thing!' first appeared in *Sunny Stories*, No. 133, 1939

'Brer Rabbit Lays in His Winter Stores' first appeared in *Sunny Stories*, No. 90, 1938

'Mr Meddle and the Snow' first appeared in *Sunny Stories*, No. 158, 1940

'One Winter Morning' first appeared in *Enid Blyton's Magazine*, No. 3, Vol. 4, 1956

'Is There Anything Particular You Want?' first appeared in *Enid Blyton's Magazine*, No. 2, Vol. 4, 1956

'Happy New Year!' first appeared in *Sunny Stories*, No. 497, 1950

'When Mr Pink-Whistle Met the Twins' first appeared in *Enid Blyton's Magazine*, No. 1, Vol. 5, 1957

'A Boy in a Thousand!' first appeared in *Enid Blyton's Magazine*, No. 1, Vol. 7, 1959

Also available:

Enid Blyton

STORIES OF
MAGIC
AND
MISCHIEF

30 stories

A spellbinding selection of magical and
mischievous tales by the world's
best-loved storyteller!

THE SECRET SEVEN

READ ALL 15 CLASSIC STORIES!

THE

SECRET SEVEN

SOLVE THE MYSTERY!

And don't miss…

The Secret Seven are back in a brand-new mystery by prizewinning author Pamela Butchart!

THE
SECRET
SEVEN

SOLVE THE MYSTERY!

Solve every puzzle, just like the Secret Seven,
in this fun book of 100 tricky codes, puzzles,
sudokus, crosswords and more!

More classic stories from the world of

Enid Blyton

The Famous Five Colour Short Stories

Enid Blyton also wrote eight short stories about the
Famous Five. Here they are, in their original texts,
with brand-new illustrations. They're a perfect
introduction to the gang, and an exciting new way to
enjoy classic Blyton stories.

Read them all!

Enid Blyton

is one of the most popular children's authors of all time. Her books have sold over 500 million copies and have been translated into other languages more often than any other children's author.

Enid Blyton adored writing for children. She wrote over 600 books and hundreds of short stories. *The Famous Five* books, now 75 years old, are her most popular. She is also the author of other favourites including *The Secret Seven*, *The Magic Faraway Tree*, *Malory Towers* and *Noddy*.

Born in London in 1897, Enid lived much of her life in Buckinghamshire and adored dogs, gardening and the countryside. She was very knowledgeable about trees, flowers, birds and animals.

Dorset – where some of the Famous Five's adventures are set – was a favourite place of hers too.

Enid Blyton's stories are read and loved by millions of children (and grown-ups) all over the world. Visit enidblyton.co.uk to discover more.